Enlighten Your Body

Enlighten Your Body

Enlighten Your Body

YOGA FOR MIND-BODY AWARENESS

By LindaChristy Weiler, M.S.

First Edition

Belle Rive Press
Nashville, TN
2004

Enlighten Your Body

First Printing 2004

Printed in the United States of America

ISBN 0-9701402 – 5 - 8

I dedicate this book
to my children, Paul and Jennifer.

Acknowledgments

A heartfelt thank you to my husband David R. Weiler
for his computer knowledge, technical support, assistance with
photographic details, and generous endorsement of this project.
Most of all, I am thankful for his encouragement
and inspiration.

I would also like to acknowledge two dear friends,
Frankie Hahn and Noel Morton,
for bringing the gift of camaraderie to my life.

CONTENTS

My duty is not to fix the world.
My duty is to fix myself.
And if, by fixing myself,
I have in any way contributed to fixing the world,
Then I have been doubly successful.
~LCW

Preface

Today's trendy versions of yoga have cute and clever names like Spinning Yoga, Yogilates, and the uplifting, if not enlightening, 'Yoga Butt!' Certainly the popularity of such programs suggests that they offer a fun and fulfilling fitness experience. But I wonder if these programs really provide a valid mind-body experience.

It seems that something essential to the experience of yoga asana has been forgotten or overlooked, and this essential element is exactly what yoga asana is all about. It is the attention given to the somatic aspect of the experience. It is the unfolding understanding of how we can apply the lessons of asana toward the evolution of the self.

Yoga asana is a somatic method created by spiritual masters. It was not created by celebrity fitness buffs or exercise physiologists. Yoga's spiritual roots suggest that these techniques are meant to accomplish something more than hard bodies and physical prowess.

Enlighten Your Body is designed to prompt inner awakenings regarding the somatic nature of the asana experience. It reminds us that asana is more about how a pose feels and less about how a pose looks. It proposes that yoga asana has the potential to reshape both the body and the mind through a somatic re-education process based on enhanced awareness.

This is not a how-to book about yoga. Instead, *Enlighten Your Body* provides an in depth examination into the mind-body component of the asana experience. It highlights the importance of introspection and contemplation during the physical practice. The reader will be convinced that the technique of yoga asana is not random, insignificant, or easily mastered.

The primary tenet of this text is that we achieve transformation through restoration by playing two seemingly opposing roles during asana – the Participant and the Observer.

When we speak of our self in terms of our anatomy, we almost always point to the heart. This universal anatomical reference indicates our belief that the 'I' consciousness abides at the center of our bodily universe. It also suggests that we identify with the body as self.

From this subjective perspective, everything else is viewed as being outside of, apart from, or existing in relationship to 'me.' This is the perspective of the Participant-consciousness. Because the Participant perspective provides our first experience as a human being living in a three-dimensional environment, it shapes our basic approach to life. For many people, this is the only perspective that they will ever use.

The Participant, as the name implies, is a doer. He operates via comparison and competition. He is goal oriented, and not particularly interested in understanding the how or why of his actions. He is often so immersed in his situation that he reacts habitually and unconsciously. This is why the Participant is incapable of viewing himself in an objective manner.

In yoga asana, we use the seeing alignment strategy to experience the Participant-consciousness. The Participant relies on visual input – how the pose looks – as the primary criteria for evaluating success in asana. He prefers the seeing alignment strategy due to its sense of immediacy. It's quick and easy, though based solely on the superficiality of image.

But there is another possible perspective which is known as the Observer-consciousness or the Witness. This perspective is valuable because it provides the impetus for growth by offering a unique and unfamiliar experience of the self. In this perspective, the self is no longer located at the center (heart or core) of one's being. This new, non-proximal vantage point diminishes the tendency toward egocentricity. It also teaches us how to approach the asana experience in fresh, new, and unfamiliar ways.

As a witness to the self, the Observer seeks to relinquish, or at least greatly reduce, the degree of his ego's involvement. He does this by experiencing the role of a detached bystander who reports the facts in a non-judgmental manner. Progression occurs as he acquires the ability to consciously curtail habitual tendencies toward tension, negativity, aggression, and sloth. Both mental and physical rigidities and weaknesses are gradually rectified and resolved. Transformation toward a healthier, more peaceful, and meaningful existence is the direct result of enhanced awareness.

The process of personal evolution through yoga asana begins with the creation of the Observer consciousness. As the Observer, we learn to sharpen our sensory skills so that we can perceive, identify, and contemplate with accuracy and specificity. Our intent is to acknowledge and understand those subtle details in our bodies, thoughts, and behaviors that were previously overlooked.

In asana, we use the sensing alignment strategy to cultivate the objectivity of the Observer. In this strategy, we rely on bodily sensations and kinesthetic awareness – how the pose feels – to guide our practice. By tuning into the consciousness of our own bodies, we can learn to make wise and reasonable choices. And we come to understand that responsible and appropriate behaviors produce a favorable effect on both our internal environment (the inner workings of the psyche and soma) and our external environment (interpersonal relationships and surroundings).

Eventually, successful integration and conscious transformation are sustained when the Participant status and the Observer status can coexist in a harmonious, symbiotic fashion. When this happens, we will be able to experience concepts like unity, connection, faith, and freedom *in our bodies*. We will understand that the body and how we view the body reflects and affects the condition of the psyche. Essentially, we are the consciousness of the living body. *We are the soma*.

This text is divided into four parts – Part One: The Self as Soma, Part Two: Creating the Observer Consciousness, Part Three: Clarifying the Psyche, and Part Four: Embodying Wholeness.

In Part One, we are introduced to the concept of the body as consciousness. This refers to the somatic manifestation of the life force. We will also examine yoga asana's potential as a structural method for personal transformation through sensori-motor learning.

In Part Two, we study a variety of perspectives that help us create the Observer consciousness. These somatic perspectives include the basic concepts of body maps, forgotten parts, the center, and the psoas. We will encounter the seeing and sensing alignment strategies, active vs. passive polarities, and the progressive notion of the edge. Finally, we will explore the significance and utility of the breath as the intermediary component in mind-body unity.

In Part Three, we begin to clarify the psyche by studying psychological issues and illusions that circumscribe our progress. We might be surprised to discover that we create our own limitations, and that they are more mental than physical. We will see how stereotypical thought processes like assumptions, beliefs, the tendency toward fear or faith, and conscious vs. unconscious intent all leave their somatic footprint in the body.

In Part Four we integrate the insights acquired from the Observer perspective with the psychological enhancements gained during the process of clarifying the psyche. We will conclude that asana is a somatic technique which teaches us to contact our bodies so that we can re-connect with our selves.

This text contains twenty-two inquiries. These are experiential activities that enhance the practical use of somatic awareness. When performing the inquiries, work gently, patiently, and consciously. Acknowledge the fact that your body didn't get into its present state of being (pain, misalignment, misuse, or malnourishment) overnight. Improvements are occurring, even if they are minute or barely noticeable. Trying to force immediate or profound change will insure detrimental results such as unintentional injury. An injury is a set back, and a set back is not the forward moving path that we seek.

During the inquiries, you might feel things in your body that you haven't felt before or haven't felt for a very long time. Bodily feedback in the form of sensation is to be expected. However, sensation is different from pain, and any amount of pain is a signal from your body that you are trying too hard. The somatic method requires constant mental surveillance. It also requires a willingness to adapt. Think in terms of possibilities, allowances, acceptance, and a willingness to endure the process for its own sake - in spite of *no guarantee* of reward or favorable results.

Though this text is designed to promote critical thinking, we should remember that yoga is, above all, an experiential process. We need not get hung up on, captivated by, or agonize over our ability or lack of ability to comprehend these concepts. Likewise, we need not get too emotionally or physically attached to the techniques themselves. I have known both yoga students and yoga teachers who are so *addicted* to yoga asana that they can't let a day go by without it!

Yoga's mind-body techniques are just that – techniques, or tools. They are not the end goal themselves. An exquisitely performed cobra pose does not necessarily indicate that a practitioner is healthy, happy, a person of integrity, or an enlightened being. Yoga asana comes with no guarantee that we will ever reach the state of nirvana or whatever it is that we are seeking. But it does provide valid healing techniques that can lead us toward it. Yoga asana is a somatic path toward restoration of one's physical, mental, and spiritual well-being.

Introduction

There are some yoga practitioners who feel that asana is the lowest rung on the ladder of Ashtanga yoga, and thus the least important practice. This belief stems from the heretofore prevalent attitude that our minds are of a higher nature than the baseness of the body. We assume that seated meditation is superior to any form of asana practice.

Thankfully, B.K.S. Iyengar has revised this single-sided view through his meticulous analysis and indisputable comprehension regarding the significance and potential of the asana experience. Still, traditional yoga schools may cringe at his bold and provocative suggestion that one can reach enlightenment through asana alone.

On one level, the view of asana as physical exercise is valid. Our bodies do get stronger, healthier, and more flexible as we activate awareness through mind-body integration. But the belief that yoga asana has no impact on spiritual development is based solely on an individual's limited understanding.

Any yoga teacher, whether experienced or novice, and any type of yoga asana practice will be perceived differently by each of the participating students. The students' limitations and belief structures affect how well they comprehend the instruction. Each student's present level of awareness determines what he or she gets from the class. The wisest students realize that the instructor is really just a facilitator or an educated guide. They understand that what you get from the experience is your responsibility.

Our experiences are largely shaped by our attitude and intention, as well as by our awareness.

Consider the motivation of each individual participating in a group studying classical Indian vocal music. One student may sing simply because she likes to sing, or because her parents want her to study cultural arts. Another may sing because she enjoys socializing with a group of friends. One may sing for ego-fulfillment (a chance to be in the spotlight), while another may sing purely to experience the connection to spirit.

Even though all of these students are practicing the same vocal methods, singing the same songs, and learning from the same instructor, their particular reaction to the learning experience arises from within their own consciousness. Each individual will get from the experience only what his present level of awareness is able to grasp. Likewise, each student will view the experience in the context that he is willing and able to accept as real.

Yoga teaches personal responsibility for everything we do in our lives, and how we approach asana provides our first lesson.

Asana is a process of reflection and contemplation upon the body. It is also a process of understanding and evolving the self. As we begin to acknowledge the details of who we are, what we are, and how we operate, we will be able to make wise decisions. Wise decisions are conscious choices. Wise decisions support our journey along the path of optimal health and well being. Ultimately, each of us is responsible for our own health, happiness, and the quality of our relationships.

What is the *soma?*

The *soma* is the self experienced as a body. The *soma* represents the individual self expressed as consciousness abiding within a body, as it experiences relationships through interactions with its internal and external environments via sensory perception. *Somatics* is the science of studying the soma

---

PART ONE
The Self as Soma

Almost every yoga instructor presents the techniques for asana separately from the techniques for meditation. By doing so, an instructor unintentionally suggests that the body and the mind are two distinctly unique entities. All too often this separation is grossly misunderstood, even by the most sincere and devoted yoga practitioners. Phrases like "I am not this body" can lead one to believe that the body is insignificant, undesirable, or unnecessary. Unfortunately, this misinterpretation results in the false belief that the ultimate goal of yoga is to transcend the body.

Scientists and doctors label the body as remarkable in its ability to self-regulate and regenerate. But the average person's primary body-related goal is merely an enhanced appearance. For the most part, we take our bodies for granted. We fail to fully appreciate the body's potential capabilities.

Though we might give lip service to the body as being our temple, we generally conclude that the body is nothing more than a time-consuming maintenance problem. Even the mass media's idealized image of human perfection in terms of beauty, fitness, and abilities is unrealistic and harmful. This unattainable standard makes us feel inferior. Too often, it causes us to despise our bodies and to belittle our selves.

The general consensus is that any truly worthwhile endeavor originates in the psyche. Ideas are associated with the kingdom of the mind. Ordinary, everyday experience is the domain of the body. Intellectual status is considered infinitely superior to the more or less automatic (yet essential) somatic functioning that supports the body's life.

The separation of mind-body unity originates with the common belief that consciousness is an exclusively mental attribute. We reserve the term subconsciousness for reference to the body, or for things that we can't quite grasp in our minds. We tend to think that subconscious means the opposite of conscious, but this is not an altogether accurate deduction. Conscious refers to the awareness of one's own existence. Subconscious means not wholly conscious, but still capable of being made conscious.

For example, autonomic or involuntary bodily processes are subconscious functions that occur outside of or beyond our normal state of awareness. But these functions do include an element of consciousness, or at least potential consciousness. Thus the terms conscious and subconscious indicate different levels of awareness which vary by degree or by form.

Eastern philosopher Yuasa Yasuo coined the term 'dark consciousness' to represent the functioning and processing that occurs beyond our ordinary awareness. He proposes that transformation of the self occurs through successful integration of the bright consciousness (mental processes) with the dark consciousness (autonomic, somatic-based processes). This theory suggests that personal evolution *via a practical method that utilizes the body* will enhance the psyche and nourish the spirit (Yuasa, 85).

Yoga asana and other practices of embodiment are psycho-somatic techniques that acknowledge the true significance and value of our bodies. These techniques focus on developing enhanced sensory awareness as a form of biofeedback. We learn to access somatic material so that we can understand and improve the body, the mind, and the self. Through mind-body methods, we gain the opportunity to realize our potential in a meaningful existence.

CHAPTER ONE

The Wisdom of the Body

"You haven't really lived until you've done something you regret." I wasn't exactly sure what the professor meant by this statement, but it certainly gave me something to think about. And I was not alone. The entire auditorium filled with unsophisticated undergraduates fell silent as we all began to reflect upon our lives.

Most of us had registered for Psych 101 simply because it was required for graduation. I, for one, didn't know the first thing about Psychology, and I doubted whether the course would be very interesting or applicable. Yet I found myself captivated by the professor's extraordinary opening remark. I was intrigued, but I was not altogether in agreement.

The professor's statement bothered me. It bothered me because it conflicted with my belief that life was all about improving ourselves as we advance through the years. Maybe I was being naïve or sentimental, but I thought that as we lived our lives we should try to become better humans. I thought we transitioned into adulthood by learning to do what was right. Yet he seemed to suggest that some sort of adult status was attained by doing something wrong - something that you wish you hadn't done. I was perplexed by his implication that the true road test of an adult was found by making mistakes and experiencing the negativity of regret.

In spite of my initial indignation, his comment piqued my curiosity. I had this nagging feeling that there was something insightful or even enlightening hidden within the semantics. I also knew that I would not be able to make peace with this disturbing dilemma unless I could *experience* it for myself. It wouldn't be enough to analyze or intellectualize the concept. Somehow I would have to contact the essential nature of the 'regrets consciousness' to truly understand the significance of his statement.

It seemed that the most practical and timely technique available was visualization. Using my own imagination and creative consciousness, I could take a meditative journey into the inner workings of the psyche and the soma. To do this, I tried to recall the distinct memories of my thoughts, emotions, and somatic sensations surrounding a regretful situation from my past. As realistically as I could, I examined the circumstances and re-experienced the details of the event in my mind. I was all too aware that a part of me wasn't very happy that I had reopened

3

my personal Pandora's Box filled with unresolved psychological dilemmas.

As I contemplated the unsettling nature of these memories, I noticed that a very odd phenomenon had begun to take place in my body. Physically, I was feeling a bit compressed, squeezed, and stifled. The tension level in my whole body had risen. My breathing was choppy and confined to the chest. My throat tightened and my shoulders hunched. The back of my neck was swallowed up as if I were drowning. I felt the need to struggle.

Both mentally and physically, my natural state of comfort and calmness had abandoned me. My body, just like my mind, was re-living the experience of past regrets. The amazing part was that *the somatic response had been evoked by the thoughts that were in my mind!*

This simple experiment was important because it showed me a whole different perspective. It produced an innovative way of thinking about the connection between my body and my mind. I came to the conclusion that concepts are more than intellectual ideas. Concepts have a somatic component that coincides with the original psychological impulse. As embodied entities, we have the capacity to experience concepts in our bodies.

My findings from this experiment also gave me insight into the deeper meaning of my Psychology professor's opening statement. For one thing, I realized that I didn't want to live my whole life carrying the psychic weight of any sort of regrets upon my shoulders. Keeping a secret, telling a lie, or dwelling in the muck and mire of negative qualities like enmity and aggression are a heavy burden to bear. Furthermore, the things that we regret become energetic vampires that slowly and continually drain our life force. The need to conceal, to patrol, to attack or to wound, and to seek protection by constructing interpersonal barriers produces a state of self-induced imprisonment.

It became clear to me that the experience the professor spoke of doesn't end with the *negativity* of the regrets. It ends only when the experience of the 'regrets consciousness' has been resolved, ratified, and integrated into the essential nature of one's self. The important thing is how we interpret the outcome of the experience. Our lesson is found in what we learn from our regrets.

How we handle our regrets determines whether we are a villain, a victim, or a saint. The way we choose to respond to feelings of uncertainty and unsettledness is what defines our character. But how we handle our regrets is more than just a behavioral response or a cognitive process. How we handle our regrets makes its mark in our physical bodies, for movement in the psyche leaves behind a somatic footprint.

If we can neutralize the negativity of the regret consciousness through a reasonable and responsible course of action, there is potential for a highly positive outcome. Rectifying our regrets is what makes us a competent and responsible adult.

When we have done something that we regret, we experience a negative somatic stress response. This response coincides with the unsettling mental experience of inner-conflict. A tension-filled soma and an agitated psyche are trying to inform us that our business in this circumstance is unfinished. The peculiar thing is that unless the body's sensational response is profound or acute, we often don't even notice it.

We are a society that lives almost exclusively in our heads, having little respect for the wisdom of our bodies. We are so engrossed with cognition – always thinking, plotting, planning, manipulating, and negotiating - that we tend to be unaware of the subtle sensations which signal how our bodies are reacting to our thoughts. If we do acknowledge bodily tension or psychic trauma, we try our best to suppress or ignore it. We hope that the physical symptoms and the mental regrets will just go away.

Yet we are creatures that want and need to feel good about ourselves. We prefer living in a state of comfort and harmony. The only way that we can accomplish this is by extinguishing the effects of psycho-somatic stress. If we want to be healthy and happy, negative somatic responses need to be addressed and neutralized. We need to relax in order to recover.

The Importance of Relaxation

Relaxation is the natural state of human embodiment. Relaxation is desirable because anything we do can be done better if we are relaxed. Relaxation is beneficial because it helps us to detach from the perceived dramatic nature of life. It provides a peaceful state in which we can restore our energy and our volition.

When the relaxed nature abides within us, we experience somatic sensations associated with the concept of peace. The breath is steady and the body is free from unnatural tension. Psychological qualities include inner tranquility, responsibility, acceptance, connection, direction, freedom, and integrity. These qualities portray the well adjusted adult consciousness.

To acquire or restore a peaceful existence, we seek out techniques like yoga to induce relaxation. Whether the origin is physical or psychological, somatic symptoms of distress often motivate us to attend our first yoga class. A majority of people who practice yoga do so to relieve stress. Though they begin practicing yoga to gain relief from what ails them, these students soon realize that pain, anxiety, and discontent are just symptoms.

It doesn't take long for neophyte yogis to understand that what they need is restoration through relaxation. What they are seeking is attunement. They are looking for redemption. They want to be able to live life in a way that is comfortable, enjoyable, meaningful, and worthwhile. In essence, they are seeking a way to make amends for their past regrets.

CHAPTER TWO

Somatic Awareness

A good role model is hard to find. But I'm always on the lookout. When I come across someone who does something very well, I pay attention. I try to identify exactly what makes each person an adept.

It has been my experience that most everyone has at least one area of expertise. I have found people with beautiful enunciation, healthy relationships, and good eating habits. I have found people who are remarkably talented when working with animals. Once I met a lady who was a wiz at hair and make-up techniques. I know it's incredible, but I actually found someone who has the gift of both perfect posture and perfect gait!

You never know when and where good role models will present themselves. And you can never anticipate the lesson they have to teach you. For example, one day a yoga student brought her college-aged daughter to my yoga class. Initially, I was tickled to see their physical and behavioral similarities. They had similar body types. They were exactly the same height. They smiled alike. They even walked alike. They both seemed happy and well adjusted. The best part was that they obviously enjoyed being together. The sweet familiarity they shared was something that only a long term bond could provide. I could tell that this beautiful relationship had been carefully cultivated. Since I am a mother, I was particularly interested in the mother's role in this relationship. I thought maybe I could learn something useful from her.

There was no doubt that this mother adored her daughter. But she didn't smother her daughter. She gave the daughter space to ask her own questions and find her own answers. In return, the daughter didn't need to cling to her mother or challenge her. She didn't need to exert her independence because she had already been granted freedom. The daughter knew that she was unconditionally loved and accepted.

I could see that I needed to make some changes in myself if I wanted to have this type of relationship with my daughter when she was a teenager. I needed to start investing time and effort into nourishing our relationship. By amending my current behavior, I would be laying the groundwork for our future relationship. I am hoping that this bit of observational learning has already helped me become a better mother.

We can improve ourselves by studying others. When we observe other people, we get to take part in their experiences without being directly involved. We have the chance to view the world through different eyes. This provides a new perspective that offers original ideas and creative solutions. Through observation, we learn new ways of doing things or new ways of thinking about things. If we are resourceful, we will use these insights to make improvements in ourselves.

Information acquired through observing others is an efficient way to learn and to grow. We grow by making changes in our own behavior and cognition. But we need to know something about ourselves if we want to make changes in ourselves. We need to have an idea of who we are right now. So the fundamental question we must ask is "Who am I?"

At first we think the answer is pretty straight forward. "I am my job, my gender, my age, my weight, height, and hair color. I am further defined by my relationships, accomplishments, and moods." But this is not meant to be a simple question with an obvious answer. It is actually a highly esoteric question that deserves an equally esoteric answer. Indeed, it is the classical question of 'soul searching' – and it is something that many people ponder for a lifetime.

Yes, it is a difficult question. But it need not be an impossible question. In fact, we're going to confront this question from a very practical perspective. Let's start with the basics. First of all, each of us has a body. Believe it or not, this body is full of information about our health, our emotions, our ideas, our past experiences, our potential, etc. The problem is that most of us don't know how to access this bodily information. Most of us never make use of the innate wisdom stored within our bodies. We call this natural awareness *the soma*, or the self experienced as a body. To learn about ourselves, we start by observing the soma.

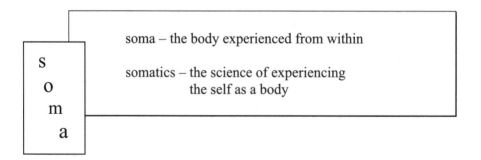

soma – the body experienced from within

somatics – the science of experiencing
the self as a body

s
o
m
a

Basic Concepts of Mind-Body Unity

Yoga, massage, Feldenkrais, Tai Chi, Pilates, and Therapeutic Touch are all examples of mind-body methods for health and fitness. Mind-body modalities use the body's physical framework as reference. Their goal is to restore our human potential using enhanced bodily awareness. All of these modalities contain five basic concepts that cultivate the harmonious state of mind-body unity. The concepts are Somatics 101, Relaxation, Effortless Effort, Sensory Awareness, and Responsibility. These seemingly simple concepts compose the basic techniques for re-education through sensori-motor learning.

➤ (1) <u>Somatics 101</u>: Somatics is the science of experiencing the self as a body. To tap into the consciousness of the soma, or the embodied mind, we must abide by three simple rules of etiquette which are *Be still. Be quiet. Be present.*

  We are consciously present when we are truly attending to the current moment, experience, sensation, feeling, and thought. We are consciously present when the mind is focused exclusively on what the body is doing. 'Being present' means that the soma and psyche are working in harmony and unison. This is the opposite of daydreaming.

➤ (2) <u>Relaxation</u>: The natural state of embodiment is relaxation. A relaxed body has a better chance of being a healthy body that is capable of continual restoration. Conscious relaxation produces a mind that is deliberately neutral or clear. Neutral refers to the mental qualities of openness, acceptance, and tolerance. When we are thinking clearly, we are not clouded by expectations, judgments, irrational, or even overtly rational thinking.

  Physical relaxation also improves the body's capacity for proper respiration. A tense body harbors a tense mind and creates restricted breathing. A relaxed body reflects a neutral mind and supports natural respiration. It is important to remember that anything we do can be done better if we are relaxed.

➤ (3) <u>Effortless effort</u>: If we apply too little effort in our endeavors, we lack adequate capacity. We have underestimated the necessity. If we apply too much effort in our endeavors, we inhibit advancement. We have overextended or wasted our capabilities. Therefore, the most prudent path is one of moderation. We should try to do our best, but avoid trying too hard.

> (4) <u>Sensory Awareness</u>: Sensory awareness is the ability to consciously attend to all sensory input. This technique is the stepping stone for self discovery through mind-body methods. Sensory awareness rests on the belief that the body itself is consciousness. It proposes that this 'wisdom of the body' plays an integral part in personal transformation.

Normally, the majority of our mental stimulation comes from visual input. The mind operates via observation and contemplation on what the eyes see. But the realm of the body is based on sensation. The body's consciousness relies on input from touch, taste, smell, and hearing - as well as visual input. The body also gathers much of its data from kinesthetic awareness and somatic insights.

Unfortunately, many of us operate in an illusory state of debauched kinesthesia (mistaking poor body use as good body use). Others suffer from sensorimotor amnesia (a learned response in which we have lost awareness of sensation in certain body parts).

> (5) <u>Responsibility</u>: We have the freedom to choose our own actions, behaviors, thoughts, perceptions, and beliefs, but we must bear the responsibility for the choices we make. To be responsible is to be accountable, trustworthy, or obligatory. The key idea behind the concept of responsibility is "What you make of your life is up to you."

The responsible person is a person of substance. Substance refers to one's essential nature. The 'substance' is the opposite of the 'image' – which refers to the superficiality associated with the physical appearance. Image seekers are obsessed by appearance, status, and the ego. Persons of substance are interested in ethics, integrity, and unity. As our consciousness shifts toward intuition and somatic sensation, we'll find that we no longer need to project a certain image to feel ratified.

Yoga as a Somatic Method

Yoga asana is a mind-body method that features stillness, spinal restoration, the non-verbal state, relaxation, and conscious attention to the breath. As a fitness program, yoga is unique because of its non-movement approach. When the body is still and silent during asana, external distractions are reduced. We enter into a mild state of sensory deprivation. In this altered state, mental energy becomes available for conscious use. This is a positive experience because it gives us the opportunity to slow down, relax, shift our perspective, and determine our priorities.

"You are as young as your spine" is a common adage among yoga practitioners. This saying refers to the fact that proper alignment of the vertebrae indicates a healthy nervous system and a healthy body. The restoration of the spine's natural, youthful flexibility is yoga's primary physical goal. During a hatha yoga class, the spine is folded, arched, twisted, and stretched. All of these maneuvers are done in an attempt to restore proper structure and natural functional capacity to the spine.

The non-verbal state plays a significant role in mind-body awareness. When we are not talking, we do more listening. When we are listening, we become an Observer. In yoga asana, listening re-directs our awareness toward the internal environment of the body. As our awareness of the external world is temporarily suspended, we begin to notice that our own body has a voice - *though it does not speak in words*. The non-verbal state produces a type of silence that allows us to hear things that we haven't heard before.

Much of the physical emphasis in asana is devoted to the experience of relaxation. Relaxation includes tension-free physical consciousness and disciplined mental awareness. Only when the mental self is no longer emotionally charged and the physical self is no longer over-stimulated may we attain the state of comfortable, blissful relaxation. The cue "relax," when given in a yoga class, implies both physical comfort and psychological detachment.

Conscious attention to the breath provides the integral, unifying component in the asana experience. The process of respiration reveals awareness of the existence of the life force. Qualities of respiration provide insight into an individual's current mental, emotional, and physical states.

Yoga promotes a greater understanding of life by providing a greater understanding of our bodies and our selves. Understanding life is very different from reflexively reacting to life. As we progress in our understanding, we begin to make wise decisions. Wise decisions are not random or habitual. They are conscious decisions, based on sincerity and clarity of intent. The person who makes wise decisions is living in a state of mind-body harmony.

CHAPTER THREE

Sensori-motor Learning

"Pay no heed to what others think. Listen only to the voice of the self." One of my most devoted yoga students told me that lately she'd read a lot of statements like this. Even though they were often written by spiritual masters, she felt they present a conundrum. She said that the statement seems to imply that "If I concentrate on doing what's best for me, I will be fulfilling my personal duty or my life's mission." She had a good point. That does seem true.

Then she argued that "If I do what's right for me while completely disregarding others, I would be acting selfishly." She had another good point. That also seems true. Her problem was that these two supposed truths didn't jibe. Now she was asking me what I thought about this dilemma. She chuckled when I told her that I thought this is one of the most excellent questions I've ever heard!

If you've studied any yoga-related philosophy books or read any spiritual or psychological self-help books, no doubt you've come across this sort of statement. The wording might be different, but basically the message is the same. You are directed to "follow your inner guidance." You are supposed to "stop listening to others and start listening to your self; stop doing for others and start doing for your self." You are told that "service to the self is the best form of service to others."

Unfortunately, many of us mistake or distort the true meaning of this statement. I don't think that the misinterpretation is intentional. I believe that the majority of us are truly trying our best to understand. I believe that we sincerely want to do the right thing. But it's very easy to twist these philosophical statements around for our convenience. We get them to say what we want them to say. We adjust them so that they sanctify the egocentric consciousness. And we are often unaware that we have done this.

Our confusion comes from the use of the word 'self.' We are conditioned to think that the self refers to myself, as in 'me.' From this perspective, self is all about separation, and separation is the realm of the ego. But we are not talking about the ego. We are not being told to follow the advice of that which is ambitious, judgmental, and has something to prove. No, that is not the self that we are seeking. What we are talking about is the self that is a part of all other selves. We are referring to the universal self portrayed as a unique individual. From this perspective, it's easy to see that what is right for 'me' will indeed be in the best interest of all.

The next question is how do we access the voice of the self? How do we distinguish the voice of the self from the voice of the ego? If emotions get fired up, we're probably listening to the ego. If we are excused from all of our duties, responsibilities, relationships, and regrets, it is the ego talking. If our intent involves controlling others or aggrandizing ourselves, again – it's the ego. The ego entices us to do things that feature 'me,' promote 'me,' and make 'me' look better, bigger, more beautiful, more intelligent, more spiritual, or more powerful than someone else.

When we understand that the true self is composed of both you and me, we will pause to consider how our actions affect others. We will choose our thoughts and behaviors with care so that they reflect unity, harmony, and benefit to all. If our choices are based on a combination of what seems right, reasonable, and responsible, we are most likely listening to the self.

We can learn the same lesson in yoga asana. I regularly remind my students that "Your body is your first and best teacher. I am your second teacher." In effect, I am telling them to rely on the self. Surprisingly enough, the hardest part of asana is accessing the voice of the self. As we practice the poses, how do we know if we are listening to the voice of the self or the voice of the ego?

If we have a need to achieve, to perform, to dominate and control our body in the pose, we have accessed only the façade of the self. We are listening to the ego. This practitioner does not yet understand that no matter how imperfectly any asana is executed, it may in fact be quite a perfect experience for that individual.

When we honor our bodies, we honor the self. We honor the self by listening to the self. Yes, we may be influenced by others. Yes, we may be guided by the yoga teacher. But ultimately, we must listen to and follow the voice of the self. To achieve transformation through yoga, we must have the courage and conviction to seek out and act upon what is right and best for the self.

An individualized practice

One of the first things any yoga practitioner should learn and learn well is that asana is an   individualized practice. It is not a standardized technique in which one size fits all. Yoga asana is not about squeezing your body into a certain pose. It is not about imitating the capabilities of someone else's body or recreating a picture you saw in a book. Asana is not meant to be a competition or a performance. Instead, it is a means of discovering the details of the self using the vehicle of the body.

Yoga asana helps us learn about our selves by learning about our bodies. It helps us to identify our subconscious tendencies or habitual ways of being that no longer support growth. These self-limiting tendencies affirm our existing limitations. Their job is to maintain the status quo. But by doing so, they restrict our capacity for growth. The conundrum is that we cannot grow, change, or improve ourselves if we aren't aware of what it is that needs to be changed. If we want to remove these self-imposed limitation devices, we must first identify and acknowledge their presence.

There are three reasons why habitual tendencies are so hard to eradicate. The first reason is that we don't like to acknowledge that the problem lies 'within.' As a form of self-preservation, we deny the possibility that we are the source of the negativity. Instead we find comfort in the conviction that problems happen to us. We are quick to blame our problems on others or on life itself. Problems come from 'somewhere out there.' Problems exist outside of or apart from 'me.' This viewpoint indicates that we are not willing to accept personal responsibility for our failures or faults. As a result, we never figure out the root cause of the problem.

The second reason is that habitual tendencies come in many different varieties. They may be physical, mental, emotional, or behavioral. Though these tendencies produce limitations, they may be socially acceptable. They may even be socially approved. Some habitual tendencies are driven by needs or desires. Others habitual tendencies are ways of subconsciously honoring our parents or other important role models by imitating their behaviors.

The third reason is that these tendencies are deeply imbedded into our psyches and somas. Habits are so automatic that we normally don't even know they exist. They are our personal characteristics and mannerisms. Whether they are good or bad, we rely on these habitual tendencies to identify 'me.'

These three reasons point to the main problem we confront when trying to make changes in the self. The key stumbling block in the process of introspection is that *we have already overlooked that which we are looking for.* In spite of our sincere attempts at self-contemplation, we continue to overlook details about ourselves that would seem obvious to our family and friends.

Even when we honestly believe that we are actively seeking them, these habits continue to elude us. We are pre-programmed with an enigmatic tendency to overlook that which is too near to us. This includes the details of the self. Our minds believe that these details are an integral part of what we consider to be 'me.' Subconscious habits are so much a part of our self-identity that we cannot differentiate between what is 'me' and what are merely 'my habits.'

Complementary Forms of Consciousness

For introspection to be effective, it must contain two opposing aspects of consciousness. These aspects are opposing but complementary. One portion of consciousness *participates* in the experience of the self as a body. (This aspect represents the ego.) Another equally important portion of consciousness *observes* the experience of the self as a body.

The standard and most commonly used aspect of consciousness is the Participant. For the majority of us, the Participant-consciousness shapes our basic approach to life. The problem is that the Participant-consciousness is so caught up in the world of 'me' and 'mine' that he is incapable of accurate self reflection.

Remember, our initial and moderate goal in the practice of yoga asana is to look for that which we have previously overlooked. To do this, we need to change our perspective. We need to let go of the habitual Participant-consciousness that favors egocentricity, separation, competition, and conquest.

We must learn to create and employ the Observer-consciousness. The Observer or the Witness views the self and the world from a very different perspective. This perspective is characterized by objectivity, non-judgment, and detachment. The Observer-consciousness gives us a glimpse into the coexisting duality of the seer and what is seen. It lets us begin to understand that complementary aspects constitute the state of wholeness.

❖ Inquiry # 1a: "Observing the hands"

Concept: In this inquiry, we separate the roles of Participant and Observer.

Discussion: To contact the Observer or Witness perspective, you will temporarily relocate your consciousness to the back of the head. This new location will become your 'center' or the vantage point from which you view the self and the world. Positioning the self in this location, you become an outside observer or a detached witness that has no personal involvement with directing bodily movement.

Directions: Sit in a comfortable cross-legged position with prayer hands in front of the heart. Keep the spine erect and the head upright. Sit heavily on the sitz bones. As you inhale, lift the arms slowly upward until they are fully extended. The gaze follows the hands, with the eyes leading the action. If necessary, lift or lower the chin just slightly to complete the action. As you exhale, the arms and hands slowly return to the original position in front of the heart. The gaze follows.

Notice how you can feel the hands functioning as Participant, while the Observer watches from the back of the head. The relocation of consciousness produces the experience of detachment and objectivity known as the Observer.

Inquiry # 1a:
"Observing the hands"

❖ Inquiry # 1b: "Push hands"

Concept: In this inquiry, we experience the complementary nature of duality through the somatic sensations in our hands.

Discussion: The Participant-consciousness is a more complex notion than it first appears to be. You will find that different or even opposing concepts can simultaneously coexist within the Participant. These opposing aspects, though separate and distinguishable, complement each other. They contribute to the totality of the experience.

Directions: Sit in the same cross-legged position, having the hands in prayer gesture in front of the heart. The location of consciousness now slips into the palms of the hands, producing the sensation of active involvement which characterizes the Participant. To perform the inquiry, slowly begin a steady side-to-side pushing movement. Have one hand initiate the action while the other hand allows the action to occur. Keep the forearms parallel to the floor so that the movement range is only about 3 - 5 inches in each direction.

Inquiry # 1b: "Push Hands"

As you reverse the movement from right to left and left to right, notice the opposing yet complementary nature of the participating hands. When one is active, the other is passive. When one is dominant, the other is recessive. When one is controlling or creating, the other yields. The key idea in this inquiry is the amazing ability to experience the sensation of two different forces at the same time.

Re-educating the Self

When we can balance the Observer and Participant, we are able to move freely between the states of doing and being. We take a big step toward this balanced awareness by using the sensing alignment strategy. In this strategy, our data and input are based on what we feel instead of what we see. We relearn how to trust our instincts. We also learn to release the tendency toward fear by rebuilding or restoring faith. Think of yoga asana as a process of sensori-motor re-education. As we refine our physical placement in asana, we improve our ability to engage the nervous system. Most neophyte yogis are in for an unhappy surprise when they discover that much of this engagement process is not easily accessible because it is not under conscious control.

Initially, asana produces quite a blow to one's ego! Physical limitations become all too apparent. The new yoga students experience muscular tightness, inadequate range of motion at the joints, and a general inability to stretch, flex, or bend their bodies into position. Profound lack of accomplishment in the poses makes it obvious that they have fallen short of mastery. They cannot deny the reality of the physical incapacities, the mental dilemma, and the humbling feeling of severe incompetence. To achieve any degree of competency and success, all wannabe yogis must journey through the stages of the sensori-motor learning process.

Stages of Sensori-Motor Learning

The four stages of the sensori-motor learning process are Unconscious Incompetence, Conscious Incompetence, Conscious Competence, and Unconscious Competence.

The novice begins in the uncomfortable stage of Unconscious Incompetence. In this stage, everything is brand new and unfamiliar. To attempt the basic structure of the pose is a challenge and a chore. The student in the stage of Unconscious Incompetence sees asana as a creative form of physical exercise. It is merely a series of interesting positions or placements to be re-created in his body.

At this point, he has total disregard for the deeper somatic and conceptual nature of asana. He has no knowledge of or experience with the sensational significance of asana. Though the new student's attention capabilities are stressed to the limit, awareness and understanding are lacking. Essentially he is just muddling through, though on some bizarre level of denial, he thinks he is doing O.K.

In the next stage of Conscious Incompetence, endgaining (attaining the goal at all costs) is the norm. The student is determined to be successful by will alone. His desire to succeed is strong. Yet he finds that in spite of these good intentions, the technique still seems unattainable.

Energy is wasted, breathing is restricted, and there is unnecessary tension and rigidity in the musculature. Absolutely nothing is easy or natural. He desperately wants his body parts to work in harmony, but it doesn't happen. Soon enough, he realizes that the lack of accomplishment comes from his own shortage of neuromuscular connections. Neither mental nor physical processes are responding correctly because there is a lack of conscious control.

What the student does not realize is that the sense of incompetence stems from the unnecessary acts that he is unconsciously performing. As long as the student continues to approach asana from a strategy of aggression, the state of accomplishment will elude him. During this stage, the student comes face to face with his inadequacies, imperfections, negative tendencies, and lingering self doubts. Regretfully, he realizes how very incompetent he is. Asana seems uncomfortable, unmanageable, hopeless, and even useless. Due to this crushing blow to the ego, many students give up and quit during the stage of Conscious Incompetence.

Conscious Incompetence is the most arduous stage in the process of sensori-motor learning. But the student with fortitude will begin to understand that asana is not just a physical challenge. He notices that his attitude affects his performance. And he notices that his attitude is something he can control. In the stage of Conscious Competence, he will also deal with the issues of pride, the ego, and the competitive urge for domination.

Finally, after much perseverance and commitment, the truly dedicated student reaches the third stage of mastery called Conscious Competence. This stage is marked by the return of self-confidence and the acceptance of personal responsibility. Hours spent in endless repetition have yielded moments of mastery and wisdom. The student is able to maintain harmoniously balanced muscle tone while performing asana. Thoughts and emotions are also, for the most part, in a state of equanimity. Control for much of the asana experience has been shifted into the unconscious mind. Most students are content to remain at this level of awareness. They recognize a degree of mastery within themselves and they feel fulfilled.

But there is a further stage of mastery, a fourth stage called Unconscious Competence. In this stage, the lessons learned from asana practice pervade all aspects of the student's life. He has gained a better understanding of his body and himself. He knows that he learns and grows through challenge and change. He has survived a difficult protégé process that included humiliation, confusion, and long hours spent in infinite repetition and practice.

Upon reaching the stage of Unconscious Competence, the student acknowledges the depth of yoga asana. He appreciates this method for approaching personal boundaries with the intent of ongoing growth. In this stage the student has reached the realm that merges duality. He can actively participate and objectively observe at the same time. He is a mind that is embodied. He is consciousness that delights in animating matter.

Essentially, asana's somatic learning process is a discipline. We are learning to recognize our somatic, cognitive, or behavioral tendencies as they occur. We are learning to re-direct the somatic, cognitive, or behavioral response in a more desirable or appropriate way. With practice, this redirection or re-education occurs almost instantaneously. Eventually, it overrides or replaces the original tendency. This is the process of sensori-motor learning. It is conscious somatic change for the purpose of growth and evolution.

Whether we want to correct a bad habit or whether we want to attain enlightenment, an orientation toward mind-body unity is a necessary pre-requisite. For sensori-motor learning to be completely effective, sensations of improvement must be reorganized in one's physical consciousness (the soma) and redefined in one's mental consciousness (the psyche).

When both the psyche and the soma recognize the changes as self, subconscious integration is complete. The self no longer recognizes the old placement or the old behavior as 'me.' The old 'me' has been replaced by the new 'me,' which operates via the new placement and the new behavior.

Enlighten Your Body

PART TWO

Creating the Observer Consciousness

No matter which pose we are practicing, the process of
yoga asana begins with the intent to filter out unnecessary
distractions. As we shed distractions, we begin to notice the immediate
somatic material. This is not an easy endeavor, for our lifestyle demands
that we operate in spite of and in response to over-stimulation and
sensory overload.

We are a society of extremely busy people! We've grown
accustomed to operating in high gear. We all try to juggle as many
projects as we possibly can. The ability to multi-task is considered the
sign of an important and productive individual. Unfortunately, the quick
and snappy pace of modern day society does not coincide with a human
being's natural rhythm. If we could learn not to be distracted or irritated
by the steady bombardment of external influences, our lives would be
easier and less stressful.

The truth is that we actually function better and accomplish more if
we are not trying to attend to too many things at once. But the
distractions aren't going to go away. So we must learn how to deal with
them. We must create our own sense of tranquility. We must establish a
pace for ourselves that is comfortable and manageable. We can
accomplish these goals by choosing which stimuli to attend to and which
stimuli to ignore.

In yoga asana, the stillness of the body and the silence of the mind
provide a tranquil inner environment. This peaceful environment helps us
maintain our focus. When sensory stimuli are reduced, subtle somatic
indicators are no longer overshadowed by mental chatter and physical
discomfort. The soft voice of the soma comes into consciousness and
makes itself heard. By creating a degree of tranquility in our internal
environment, we lay the groundwork for producing a shift in awareness.
This is the foundation of the Observer-consciousness.

These are two separate yet complementary ways of creating the
Observer-consciousness in yoga asana. The first emphasizes technical
precision based on proper placement and alignment. In this approach, the
student strives to reproduce a near replica of an established standard
shape of the asana in his own body. The theory is that by creating the
external shell of the form, the associated inner awareness will be brought
forth.

Body maps, forgotten parts, and the 'seeing alignment' strategy are somatic approaches that cultivate the awareness of external form. Our consciousness of the physical body's boundaries serves as a starting point to understand structure and alignment in asana. In this case, the emphasis is on the external form, and we build the pose based on image recognition or how the pose looks. Our hypothesis is that outer form determines inner substance.

The second approach emphasizes the individual's unique inner sensational experience in the pose. In this method, the construction of the outer form is built in response to inner sensation, emotional stability, and deep personal awareness. The center, the psoas, and the 'sensing alignment' strategy prompt somatic awareness by focusing our consciousness on the body's core structures and associated state of being.

A good way to understand this approach is to keep our eyes closed as we perform each pose. Practicing with the eyes closed allows no visual input to distract or assist us. The practitioner focuses exclusively on what he feels – not on what he sees. The theory is that by creating kinesthetic awareness of the appropriate somatic sensations, the body will automatically produce a perfected asana. In this case, our hypothesis is that inner substance determines outer form.

If our initial and moderate goal in asana is to look for that which we have previously overlooked, it makes sense that the awareness process should start with the study of that which is most apparent. Let's begin our somatic journey with the tangible and clearly obvious part of the asana experience, which is the body itself.

CHAPTER FOUR
Body Maps

In yoga we say that "you are as young as your spine." What this statement really means is "you are as young as your spine is *flexible*." The truth of this statement becomes most apparent when we observe the rigidity of many elderly persons' spines. This rigidity often results in limited range of motion, diminished flexibility, as well as stiffness, slowed movement, and back pain.

Conversely, one can observe the posture and movements of a pre-school child whose loose, natural spinal column still allows wonderful flexibility, full range of motion, and a sense of comfortable, easy movement. Psychologically, the person with a loose, flexible spine considers movement to be a joy, whereas the person with a rigid spine considers movement something to be avoided.

The original yoga tradition recognized asana as a practical program for restoration and maintenance of natural spinal flexibility. With regular, gentle practice of yoga postures *you can help yourself* feel better. Movement will become a joy instead of a chore. Gradually, you will begin to notice self-improvement on many levels - physically, mentally, emotionally, and spiritually.

Ideally, to maintain a young spine, your spine should be bent in six directions each day. These include forward and backward bending, lateral bending to the right and left, and twisting to the right and left.

To reconnect with the body and to restore natural spinal flexibility, we must start with some basic concepts of anatomically proper posture. To determine precise, safe, and accurate placement in yoga asana, we should be familiar with the essential bony landmarks and the somatic concept of anatomical lines. Bony landmarks in the body's skeletal system help us to locate body parts and assist in accurate execution of placement cues. Anatomical lines prompt a feeling of connection and interrelationship through the body-as-a-whole. These concepts help us create a mental image or 'map' of our own bodies.

When the body is viewed from the side, we see a series of palpable bony landmarks that can be used as markers for optimal vertical alignment. These bony landmarks include the outside of the ankle, the outside of the knee, the outer edge of the hip, the side of the ribcage, the side of the shoulder girdle, and the ear. Bony landmarks remind us that our bodies are more than just the superficial image created by our muscles and skin.

The perception of the body as its skeleton is a useful strategy for engaging deeper consciousness. By visualizing bodily action as the movement of skeletal bones, we avoid the tendency toward overuse of the muscles. For example, when the skeletal body is held in a static stretch, we maintain this position by visualizing connections and configurations between the intersecting bones. We also give special attention to the precise positioning of the joints.

Anatomical lines are imaginary lines that connect bony landmarks. Anatomical lines are a way of visualizing continuity between the body's parts. In yoga asana we use anatomical lines as a way to induce proper placement of body parts in relationship to one another. At first we are only able to visualize these connections in terms of generalized parts such as the foot or head. Though this type of visualization provides only a hazy image, it is still a good way to start learning about the connections and interrelationships within our bodies. As we learn to refine our placement via specific bony landmarks, the image of an anatomical line is revised. Gradually, through enhanced awareness, we will comprehend the finer gradations necessary to achieve more precise anatomical alignment.

The most common anatomical line uses bony landmarks to determine standing vertical alignment (see photo above). Other anatomical lines

include pelvis-to-foot and shoulder-to-finger tip lin
connection of shoulder to hip (or more specifically, the
frontal hip bone) helps keep the torso squared so that the ...
shoulders are aimed in the same direction.

| shoulder to finger tip | shoulder to hip | hip to foot |

❖ <u>Inquiry # 2: "Palpating the skeletal structure"</u>

Concept: In this inquiry, we learn to visualize connections and interrelationships in the body through a combination of 'see and feel' or 'observe and touch' techniques. Though this inquiry relies heavily on self-palpation, it also uses visual input. Visual input helps us create a mental memory of bony landmarks, imaginary anatomical lines, and the body's general structure.

During this inquiry, do not depend on a mirror to provide visual feedback. Instead, look directly at your own body. This subjective experience will help you learn the locations and connections between bodily parts. To perform the inquiry, look at the photos of these three poses and then create the pose with your own body. Follow the directions for each pose.

❖ Inquiry # 2a: "Seated staff pose"

The seated staff pose shows an example of an anterior anatomical line that connects the ASIS (frontal hip bone) to the kneecap, and the kneecap to the second toe.

Inquiry # 2a:
Seated staff

Directions: Sit on the floor with your legs stretched out in front of you. Palpate the frontal hip bones (anterior superior iliac spine or ASIS), the kneecaps (patella), and the bones of the second toes - all the way to the tips of the toes. Look at the specific location of these bony landmarks while your fingers explore the skeletal structure. Now close your eyes and perform the same palpations as before – ASIS, kneecaps, second toes. This will solidify the mental image of the bony landmarks that comprise this anterior anatomical line.

Finally, sit up straight so that your weight rests firmly on the sitz bones. Hands may be placed on the floor at your sides. Flex the feet and notice how the front side of the legs is actively contracting. Now focus on the image and sensation of length and extension in the backside of the legs.

❖ Inquiry # 2b: "Seated forward fold pose"

The seated forward fold pose shows an example of a posterior anatomical line that connects the sitz bones to the back of the knee, and the back of the knee to the center of the back of the heel.

Inquiry # 2b: "Seated forward fold"

Directions: For this pose, perform the palpations in a standing position. Locate and palpate the sitz bones. They will feel like a hard, knobby structure deep within each buttock. Because there is no bony structure at the back of the knee, rub your fingers along the hollow at the back of the knee directly behind the kneecap. Then palpate the hardness of the heel bone and notice the location of its central posterior portion.

Repeat the same series of palpations with your eyes closed. Mentally repeat the terminology to yourself as you contact each bony landmark - "sitz bone, back of the knee, center of the back of the heel."

Sit down on the floor with your legs stretched out in front of you. Keep the feet flexed. Inhale and lift the arms up to vertical alongside the ears. Exhale and slowly fold the torso forward from the hips. When you can't fold any further comfortably, release the arms to your sides and drop the head. In your mind's eye, notice the bony landmarks that demarcate the anatomical lines along the back of the legs.

Keep the posterior anatomical lines of the two legs parallel to each other. Focus on the image and sensation of length and extension along the backside of the legs.

❖ Inquiry # 2c: "Half moon pose"

In this pose, you will simultaneously experience both anterior and posterior anatomical lines. The standing leg (front view) shows an anterior line that connects the ASIS to the kneecap to the tip of the second toe. The lifted leg displays a posterior (rear view) anatomical line that connects the sitz bone down through the center of the back of the heel.

Directions: Reach down to touch the floor with the right hand, making a cup gesture so that all five finger tips contact the floor. Position the fingers a few inches in front of and lateral to the right foot. Shift your weight onto the right foot, but drag the toes of the left foot on the floor to balance.

When you feel steady, inhale and simultaneously straighten the right (standing) leg while lifting and extending the left leg. Push the left heel firmly away from the torso, keeping the left foot flexed. If you can't attain balance in this pose, stand with your back against a wall for support, or keep both hands touching the floor in front of you.

Inquiry # 2c: "Half moon pose"

anterior anatomical line

posterior anatomical line

Two additional externally-based placement concepts include the 'three primary weights' and the 'base of support.' Good postural alignment is primarily determined by the spatial relationship of three key body parts - the head, the chest, and the pelvis. These three body parts are the primary weight structures of the body. They must be balanced in vertical alignment to provide the best anatomical use.

Proper alignment of the primary weights predisposes us toward good anatomical placement of the bones, which greatly reduces the workload of the musculature. Energy requirements diminish because the body doesn't need to compensate for structural anomalies. If you have good posture, the body doesn't need to use compensation strategies for maintaining balance or movement. Because there is minimal feedback from the nervous system, good posture is characterized by a reduced amount of sensation. When the body's parts are in order, the body-as-a-whole feels lighter and movement becomes easy and effortless.

❖ Inquiry # 3: "Stacking the head, chest, and pelvis"

Concept: In this inquiry, we experience the difficulty involved with maintaining one's vertical balance when the three primary weights are deliberately moved out of alignment.

Directions: Assume a comfortable stance. Get a feel for the bodily comfort that is associated with the natural, upright, and properly stacked alignment of the three primary weights.

Shift the pelvis backward, moving it posterior to its anatomical alignment. Notice how this change affects the body's whole structure. Return the pelvis to its proper position, and shift the ribcage backward (cue: "collapse the ribs"). Notice how this change produces the necessity for compensatory adjustments in other body parts. Return the ribcage to its proper position, and shift the head back. Notice the changes that occur as the body tries to adapt its use to maintain verticality as best it can. Then return to a comfortable stance and rest.

Try the opposite adjustments. From a neutral stance, shift the pelvis forward. Notice how uncomfortable and unnatural this position feels. Return the pelvis to its anatomical position, and shift the ribcage forward (cue: "thrust the ribs"). Notice how this unnatural position produces compression in the middle back. Return the ribcage to its anatomical position, and shift the head forward. It only takes a moment to discover that this misalignment puts a dreadful strain on the neck. Finally, return to a comfortable stance and rest.

This lesson makes it obvious that a body in which the three primary weights (head, chest, and pelvis) are vertically aligned will provide optimal functional capacity and comfort.

Balance poses are a wonderful way to locate vertical alignment. They also help us perceive the freedom and ease found in proper anatomical placement of the three primary weights. When attempting a balance position, the mind constantly monitors the bodily responses via input in the form of sensations.

When the body declares that, "I'm not feeling pain. I'm not feeling anything," the mind initially interprets this as a problem. It assumes that something must be wrong because this is not the body's habitual state. "I am used to *feeling* sensations, so why don't I *feel* anything?"

At first the mind is unsure of this emptiness. It has no recollection of the body being void of sensation. It does not recognize this as a good thing, a joyful thing, *and the state of perfect balance.* Yet the state of being that is clear and free of sensory feedback is actually the desirable and sublime state of effortless effort in the pose.

Even if the three primary weights are perfectly stacked in vertical alignment, one's ability to find and maintain equanimity in the pose could be compromised if the body lacks a solid base of support. The base of support refers to the contact point(s) or part(s) of the body that connect its weight with the earth.

When standing upright on both feet, the base of support is our two feet. If we shift our weight to stand on one foot, the base of support has been changed to a single point, or foot. In single-leg standing poses, balance is more easily accomplished if we think of the foot in terms of four contact points instead of one. Both mentally and physically, balance is enhanced if we visualize the weight as being distributed among the theoretical four corners of the foot. This visualization creates the perception of a broader and more stable base of support.

When sitting on our bottom with knees bent and feet flat on the floor in front of us, we also have four points that serve as base of support – two feet and two sitz bones. A headstand performed with the head cradled in the hands and forearms resting on the floor supplies three points as base of support – the top of the head and the two elbows (or forearms). Though the base of support is the instrument of weight transference between our bodies and the earth, it need not be in direct contact with the earth. For example, if we are standing on a stool to reach for something on a high shelf, our two feet still represent your base of support even though they are not on the ground.

The base of support is an important feature in every pose because the somatic process is not instantaneous. In most cases, we do not begin to approach our potential for the pose until we have endured a period of stillness and silence. Often the limiting factor in our ability to sustain a pose is due to a weakness, misplacement, or mis-use in the base of support. For example, if we lack adequate strength and flexibility in our fingers, hands, wrists, arms, shoulders, or neck, we will not be able to persevere in the shoulderstand.

Whether we are standing on one foot, standing on two feet, sitting on sitz bones, balanced on the hands, perched on the ribcage and pelvis, or lying on our backs, the initial priority in every pose is the base of support. If the base of support does not provide a solid foundation, the best we can do is build a shaky structure. The pose might look right, but it will lack true balance. As we learn or relearn how to surrender our bodies' weight to gravity, we will truly understand the concept of the base of support.

The simplest way to re-establish camaraderie with gravity is by yielding, sinking, or letting go. When we yield to gravity, we get a sense of our own natural weight and volume. This type of surrender involves anchoring the body via the base of support. Anchoring refers to releasing the need to hold on, to lift up, to resist, or to be in control.

As we 'let go,' the first thing we become aware of is the body's heaviness and the downward movement of physical energy. But almost instantaneously that weighty sensation is balanced and counteracted by a rebounding feeling of lightness. The weight sinks while the subtle energy lifts up. We are supported (downward) while we are released (upward).

❖ Inquiry # 4: "Letting go"

Concept: In this inquiry, we experience the conscious release of the body's weight downward into the bodily base of support in a pose.

Directions: As you perform each of the poses, release your weight into the body part that is functioning as the base of support. On each exhale, silently repeat the affirmation "let go." The base of support for each pose is listed for you. Omit any pose that is too difficult.

Inquiry # 4: "Letting go"

Seated with both feet flat on the floor

4 points – two feet and two sitz bones

seated balancing boat
2 points – two sitz bones

crow pose
2 points – two hands

half wheel pose
5 points – two feet,
two hands, crown of head

tree pose >

1 point - one foot

or

4 points - four corners
of the foot

headstand >

3 points -
crown of head
and two forearms

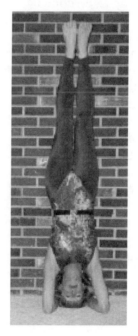

down dog pose >

4 points -
two hands
and two feet

The basic benefit of Tadasana (standing mountain pose) is experiencing the upright stance while consciously surrendering the body's weight to gravity. This simple pose teaches us the most effective and natural use of our anatomy during verticality. It also teaches us that gravity can be our ally.

The best way to describe the desired sensation of this neutral stance is to consider an insightful question regarding the quality of the pose itself. In response to the question "Should the quadriceps be actively engaged in this pose?" the ultimate answer is "no." The pose should contain no unnecessary muscular activation that is intense enough to draw your attention. The key idea is that proper skeletal alignment and optimal physical use are characterized by a minimal amount of tension and bodily sensation. In a truly balanced vertical stance, the quadriceps need not be overtly activated.

However, there are certain schools of asana that have very different ideas regarding the teaching of Tadasana. One such technique specifically emphasizes "firming the quadriceps" or "lifting the kneecaps" during this neutral stance.

The following descriptive cues make is clear that this particular teaching perspective promotes conscious engagement of the thighs during Tadasana. Notice how these cues directly suggest the experience of sensation.

Have the feeling of hugging the femur bone with the muscles of the thigh. Squeeze the thigh muscles inward and feel that you are squeezing them upward into the pelvis. Lift the hamstrings toward the buttocks. Lift the inner thighs toward the inner groins. Lift the front of the thigh toward the front groin; lift the outer thigh toward the lateral edge of the hip.

The effect of the two different somatic perspectives regarding Tadasana is obvious in the pictures below. As observers, the first thing we notice is the difference in the physical quality of the pose. The body in the first picture looks relaxed, comfortable, and natural. This body is yielding to, or working with the force of gravity.

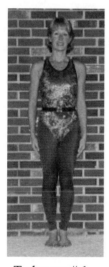

Tadasana # 1   Tadasana # 2

We get a very different feel from the body in the second picture. This body displays a more rigid quality that, though technically correct, seems a trifle unnatural. We pick up on the bodily sensation of conscious activation and alert readiness. This body looks like it is trying to lift itself up, as if to defy or resist gravity – similar to the intent of a ballet dancer. Though the figure in both pictures looks grounded and steadfast, the pose in the second picture seems a bit manufactured.

The subjective somatic experience of the individuals performing this pose is also very different. The student in the second picture feels active and alive with bodily sensation, while the student in the first picture notices a surprising decrease in sensation. When we have truly transcended the tendency toward tension by successfully yielding to gravity, there is a marked reduction in sensation – or quite possibly no sensation at all.

The mind registers this somatic state that is unbounded by sensation as a surprisingly pleasant void. It might also feel like unlimited expansion that is free of its ordinary boundaries. Tadasana provides a valuable lesson in gravity realization by promoting ease of effort through reduced sensory stimulation.

Practical cues for gravity-realization include the following:

"Yield to gravity."

"Let the weight of your body sink down into the base of support. From that stability, the body's energy is freed to rise up."

"Feel heavy and light at the same time."

"Begin with a strong foundation. Without it your house will never be stable."

"Anchor downward and lift upward."

"Anchor downward. Then release all unnecessary tension."

We feel less stressed when we relearn how to coexist in a comfortable relationship with gravity. Both posture and movement become easier when we stop resisting the gravitational presence, for gravity is the force that anchors us as it sets us free. We are amazed to discover that the true experience of gravity is heaviness and lightness at the same time!

❖ Inquiry # 5: "Same position, different pose"

Concept: In this inquiry, we learn how the body's relationship to gravity directly affects our experience in the pose by altering the body's weight distribution.

Directions: The first thing we notice is that all three of these poses require the same basic position of the body. In spite of this similarity, the actual performance of each pose feels very different. As you practice each pose, try to perceive the difference in bodily sensations that are caused by the pose's particular spatial configuration relative to gravity.

1. Seated forward fold

In seated forward fold, the torso's weight is pulled forward and downward over the legs, creating the greatest stretch on the lower back (and possibly the neck), followed by the stretch on the hamstrings.

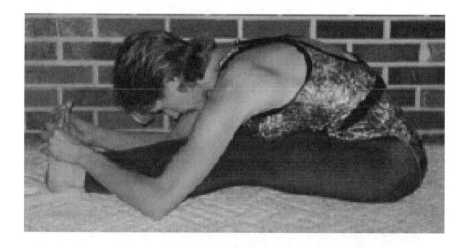

Inquiry # 5: "Same position, different pose"

2. Standing forward fold

In standing forward fold, the weight of the torso spills forward and downward out of the hips to create an intense stretch for the hamstrings.

Inquiry # 5:
"Same position,
different pose"

3. Plough

In plough, the torso's weight rests on the shoulders and neck, creating the greatest stretch at the base of the neck (and possibly in the lower back), followed by the stretch on the hamstrings.

Inquiry # 5:
"Same position,
different pose"

Consciously experiencing gravity in our bodies can also reveal certain psychological benefits. When we get a true sense of our physical weight, we become more trusting, self-confident, and calm. As we become grounded, we feel secure. A sense of security enables us to be more open and charitable in our approach to the world. We may even find the strength to surrender bad habits such as tension and frantic activity. There are numerous possible benefits found in working with the natural force of gravity. It can be our friend or it can be our foe, but it cannot be both.

All of the concepts in this chapter – bony landmarks, anatomical lines, the three primary weights, the base of support, and gravity realization – promote the psyche's ability to recognize the self as soma. Based on accessible somatic material, we then create 'body maps' or 'body schemes.' Body maps are subconscious diagrams of our bodies. Accurate or not, body maps represent the way we think about our bodies. They indicate *the way we see ourselves as a body*.

Body maps are important because they help us become more aware of the present condition of our bodies. We must identify who we are right now if we are to determine who we will be in the future. We need to know where we are if we want to plan where we are going. The concept of body maps marks the beginning of self discovery through yoga asana.

Enlighten Your Body

CHAPTER FIVE

Forgotten Parts

"Meditation in asana occurs when we can sustain conscious awareness in all body parts." My yoga students will swear that they have heard this a thousand times. Yet I keep repeating it. I want them to know what is possible. New students always have a hard time swallowing this statement. At least I know they are listening, because they flash me a dubious glance. At first, all students think that meditation only occurs in a seated position with the eyes closed.

But every now and then there is a student who wholeheartedly accepts the possibility of achieving meditation in asana. When this happens, I can see it in his eyes. The eyes become locked in position. The gaze is soft and the face is relaxed. The stillness of the gaze tells me that his awareness has gone deep inside the body to explore the somatic possibilities. Literally and figuratively, this student is 'doing his homework.' I am always happy to see someone engaging somatic awareness with the intent of transformation.

Physical characteristics that indicate a lack of awareness are much more common than those that indicate its presence. When I see eyes darting about in a random pattern, a tight jaw, toes that are pinched under, or a frozen shoulder, I know that one of two things is true. Either those body parts lack somatic awareness, or the student's mind is wandering.

One of the first steps toward enhancing our somatic awareness is recognizing where we lack it. I am sorry to report that the vast majority of us lack adequate awareness in many body parts. More often than not, our capacity to consciously engage the eyes, the jaw, the feet, the legs, and the body-below-the-belt is inadequate. The use of these body parts is so subconsciously habitual that it seems beyond conscious control. Bringing these forgotten parts into awareness will make a significant contribution to the asana experience and to the experience of daily life.

The Eyes

The sense of sight has a strong influence on how we view our lives. Our eyes perpetually provide visual input. What we see engages our consciousness. What we see is what we think about. Yet most of us don't give our gaze a second thought. This lack of visual awareness is characterized by darting, random eye movement. A gaze that cannot remain stable indicates a fragmented awareness. It suggests an inability to focus on the task at hand. It reflects a mind that is easily manipulated by the continuous stream of unregulated, intrusive thoughts.

As we practice asana, we can learn to control our gaze. We can use our gaze as a tool to enhance awareness. We do this by teaching our eyes to remain focused on a single point. For example, imagine that you are driving your car in a rainstorm. Though you are aware of the rain striking the windshield, you look past or through it. Your visual focus is on the traffic around you. You remain attentive to the task of driving. You are aware of the rain, but you are not distracted by it.

Regulating the use of the gaze is a form of sensory deprivation. In this respect, it is not unlike an extended and controlled daydream. The eyes are assigned a focal point, yet our attention is free to move elsewhere. This teaches us how to separate the use of our eyes from the use of our cognition. The exact same concept is employed during seated meditation. The difference is that when practicing formal meditation, the eyes are closed.

The ability to control our gaze allows us to divide our awareness. Divided awareness lets us create the Observer-consciousness. The problem is that the eyes do not want to be controlled. They do not want to be still, just as the body does not want to be still. But the eyes, like the body, can be brought under conscious control - in spite of plentiful distractions. When the eyes are recognized as nothing more than a particular placement of a particular body part, our consciousness does not rely so heavily on the sense of sight. We will no longer be automatically stimulated, distracted, or controlled by what we see.

Unfortunately, we begin at a disadvantage in our attempt to harness the use of our eyes. Humans are genetically predisposed to scan the environment in a predatory manner. Our gaze is automatically drawn toward any form of movement. The gaze tracks activity so that it can alert the mind about a possible threat. This is a wonderful and innate survival strategy. However, this predisposition toward a roving eye is a problem if we are interested in stilling the fluctuations of the subconscious mind.

Another reason that the eyes are hard to control is that they share a reciprocal relationship with the musculature of the neck. The activation of the eyes is inherently tied to activation of the neck, and vice versa. If we roll the eyes as far as possible to the right, we feel a corresponding urge to turn the head to the right. The muscles in the neck reflexively prepare to track the course of the gaze. Just as we can learn to separate the use of our gaze from the use of our cognition, we can learn to separate the use of eyes from the use of the neck. Ideally, the eyes should function more like the hands and the feet. The eyes should have the ability to explore the environment, act as a source of sensory information, and provide expression.

Simple eye exercises develop and train the musculature that supports the eyes. Eye exercises improve range of motion, which enlarges our peripheral view. These exercises also help us separate the use of the eyes from the use of the neck.

Be aware that eye exercises make some people feel dizzy. Others experience heaviness or discomfort around the eyes. Most everyone is surprised at their lack of ability to control the movement of the eyes.

❖ Inquiry # 6: "Eye exercises"

Concept: In this inquiry, we seek to stretch and strengthen the musculature around the eyes.

Directions: Sit upright on the floor or in a chair. Imagine that a heavy book is balanced on the top of your head. Relax the jaw, the neck, and the muscles around the eyes. Breathe slowly and deeply. As you perform the eye exercises, try not to move the head or neck. As best you can, isolate the movement in the eyes.

❖ Inquiry # 6a: "Up and down."
Look up. Look down. (10 times)

❖ Inquiry # 6b: "Side to side."
Look to the right. Look to the left. (10 times)

❖ Inquiry # 6c: "Diagonals."
Look to the lower right. Look to the upper left. (10 times) Then look to the lower left. Look to the upper right. (10 times)

❖ Inquiry # 6d: "Circles."
At a uniform rate of speed, trace a big circle clockwise with your eyes. Imagine the face of a clock and notice each number as you go around. (10 times) Trace a big circle counterclockwise with your eyes. (10 times)

The Jaw

Jaw tension is notoriously habitual in humans. The amount of tension or relaxation in the jaw is mirrored in the throat, neck, shoulders, and scalp. TMJ pain, neck pain, headaches, and teeth grinding are all indications of habitual jaw tension. If we can relearn how to relax the jaw, we will notice a corresponding slackening in the temples and the ears. The ears will feel like they are spiraling deeply into the head. A relaxed scalp will feel fuller and more comfortable.

To promote relaxation of the jaw, visualize a golf ball positioned deep in your mouth, at the very top of the throat. This image produces a feeling of spaciousness and openness between the base of the tongue and the roof of the mouth. You can imagine the soft and hard palates as a mini trampoline that suspends your brain. If the trampoline is taut, the brain feels pressed and squeezed. But if the trampoline is loose and pliable, the brain can reside comfortably in its bodily space.

Another excellent recommendation when practicing any asana is to let the jaw hang in a relaxed manner. It the jaw is truly relaxed, the top and bottom teeth will not make contact. The following exercise helps to release and stretch the affected musculature.

❖ Inquiry # 7: "Yawning"

Concept: In this inquiry, we release tension in the masseter muscle by simulating the yawning action.

Directions: Open your mouth as wide as possible, making a big yawn. Then release. Do this ten times. You can vary the position of the mouth and jaw slightly by combining the traditional yawning position with a lateral expansion.

The Lower Body

If we were to separate the body into upper and lower halves, the upper portion would win the award for intelligence and utility. We use our head, arms, and hands to make worthwhile contributions to the world. The head contains the brain and key sensory organs. Our arms and hands are capable of skilled activities. Through the arms, we reach out to make contact with the world around us. Our arms and hands also provide expression and creativity.

The body-below-the-belt is much less closely connected to one's sense of self. Basic physiological processes and motor activities don't require a lot of conscious direction. Walking seems to happen automatically. Yet conscious awareness of the proper structure and use of the pelvis, hips, legs, and feet is very important for maintaining a balanced body. A well-functioning lower body represents the ability to stand alone, to move with dignity and grace, and to do so without requiring assistance or support.

❖ Inquiry # 8: "Foot exercises"

Concept: In this inquiry, we practice foot movements to enhance flexibility and strength.

Discussion: Most fashion footwear confines the foot by squeezing the bones together. Over time, this constant compression causes the foot to become misshapen or deformed. Toes that curl under, a poorly developed arch, and a foot that appears puffy or bloated all indicate improper foot structure. When a foot's structure is sub-optimal, its functional capacity becomes impaired. The body must compensate for a foot problem by making adaptations at the ankle, knee, hip, or lower back. *A misuse in the foot is reflected throughout the body.*

Just as simple, repetitive eye exercises develop conscious control of the gaze, simple, repetitive foot exercises develop the intrinsic musculature of the foot. A thorough program of foot exercises include the basic point and flex movements, curling and pulling movements using the toes, articulation movements for the whole foot, and rotations. (During all flexion / extension movements, the second toe serves as the center line of the foot.)

Directions: Begin in a supine position. Stand the left foot on the floor and extend the right leg up toward the ceiling. After you have completed the whole series of exercises with the right foot, change leg positions and perform the exercises with the left foot. Take a short rest anytime the foot or leg becomes very fatigued.

❖ Inquiry # 8a: "Point and flex"
Alternate point and flex movements of the foot. (4 times)

❖ Inquiry # 8b: "Picking up marbles"
Begin with the foot flexed. (1) Extend the ball of the foot. (2) Reach up with the toes. (3) Curl the toes under as if picking up marbles. (4) Keep

the toes curled as you slowly pull the foot back toward the flexed position. (5) Release the toes. Perform these movements in a flowing movement (4 times). Be sure to create your own resistance with the intent of strengthening the intrinsic muscles of the foot.

❖ Inquiry # 8c: "Four foot movements"
Begin with the foot flexed. (1) Extend the ball of the foot. (2) Point the toes. (3) Release the toes. (4) Flex the foot. Perform this action (4 times) as distinct and deliberate movements.

❖ Inquiry # 8d: "Foot circles"
Circle the foot to the right. (4 times) Circle the foot to the left. (4 times) Isolate the motion in the working foot. Do not move the leg or hip.

❖ Inquiry # 8e: "Dropping marbles"
This exercise is pretty much the reverse of Inquiry # 8b: "Picking up marbles." Be sure to articulate the four positions distinctly. Begin with the foot flexed. (1) Curl the toes under tightly. (2) Keep the toes curled as you extend the foot upward. (3) Extend and separate the toes. (4) Flex the foot. (4 times)

❖ Inquiry # 9a: "Balanced bow pose"

Concept: In this inquiry, our intent is to bring subconscious somatic material (the legs) into consciousness. We want to remedy a fragmented awareness by bringing attention to the passive body parts. Note: Passive does not imply unconscious or unnecessary. Passive refers to a subconscious quality - something that has the potential to become conscious.

Inquiry # 9a: Balanced bow

Discussion: The bow is a classic back bending pose. Yoga students stereotypically perform the bow pose by over-contracting and over-arching the back. In this inquiry, we will try to diminish overuse in the back by actively involving the legs. The goal is to *match* the degree of contraction in your legs with the degree of contraction in your back. As the legs become active in the pose, they bear a portion of the load. In a balanced bow pose, the whole backside of the body participates equally.

Directions: Begin in a prone position on the floor. Bend the knees and bring your heels toward your bottom. Reach back and catch hold of the ankles or feet. As you inhale, let the feet pull backward and upward into the hands. Your body will arch into the shape of a bow. Concentrate on *matching* or equalizing the degree of contraction in your legs and back.

❖ Inquiry # 9b: "Forward folds"

Concept: In this inquiry, we learn to direct our awareness by choosing what we attend to. We will decide whether to focus on the sensation of strength or stretch in the legs.

Directions: You may choose either the seated forward fold or the standing forward fold for this inquiry. In both poses, the back of the legs are releasing and lengthening. The front of the legs are actively contracting and stabilizing. The balanced use of the opposing muscle groups support the joint and allow the body to avoid undesirable sensations. Depending on the particular needs to be addressed in the pose, we will consciously shift our perspective. We will learn that we can choose to focus on the sensation of stretch (in the back of the legs) or the sensation of strength (at the front of the legs).

If you want the experience of stretch, focus your attention on the back of the legs. Concentrate on the concept of releasing or relaxing. Visualize the anatomical line that extends from the posterior edge of the heel to the sitz bone. Consider the infinite quality of a geometric line. Apply this quality of infinite extension to the anatomical line of the legs.

If you want the experience of strength, bring your attention on the front of the legs. Concentrate on the concept of firming or lifting. Focus on increasing the contracting sensation in the front of the thigh. A good cue to intensify activation of the quadriceps muscle is "lift the kneecap."

Inquiry
9b:
"Forward
folds"

Differentiating between the intensity of the stretch component and the strength component provides a somatic barometer of how your body is reacting to the pose. This can also be used as an effective coping strategy. For example, if the stretch sensation in the hamstrings is rapidly becoming unbearable, you have two choices: You can make a *physiological* adjustment to reduce the level of intensity. This is easily accomplished by softening the knee. Or you can make a *psychological* adjustment by shifting your attention to the opposing muscle group. In this case, you would focus on the somatic sensations in the quadriceps.

❖ Inquiry # 10a: "Lower body as base"

Concept: In this inquiry, we experience the stability and support provided by the lower body. We will acknowledge the lower body's integral role in all standing poses.

Directions: In the first two sets of photographs, we see variations of the Warrior pose and the Tree pose. In these photos, the placement of the lower body is exactly the same. But the configuration of the arms is different. This change creates a variation by adding expression.

Inquiry # 10a: "Lower body as base"

Warrior
pose
variations

Tree pose
variations

In the next set of photos we see the opposite situation. Here the arms remain in the same position, but the placement of the lower body has changed. Can you see how the placement of the lower body in a standing pose determines the *basic structure* of the pose?

❖ Inquiry # 10b: "Abduction / adduction"

Concept: In this inquiry, we encounter two different strategies for creating stability and support in the lower body. All standing poses employ one of these techniques for providing a solid foundation during asana.

Directions: Study the following five poses. Then recreate the poses in your own body. Focus your attention on the somatic sensations in the lower body.

Discussion: The first two poses are the Warrior and the Pyramid. In both of these poses, the legs and feet are proximal to an imaginary line that bisects the body and the legs. The third pose is the traditional form of Nataraja, the King Dancer. Even though Nataraja is a single leg balance, both legs are purposefully drawn inward toward the body's center line. All three of these poses suggest the sensation of adduction. In these three poses the inner thighs and groin create a powerful force that anchors and supports the torso.

Inquiry # 10b: "Abduction/ adduction"

Pyramid

Warrior

King Dancer

52

In Warrior Two and the Folded Straddle pose, the feet are positioned in a wider stance. The torso's weight is pushed or pressed downward through the legs and feet, which grounds the body in the pose. In these two standing poses, abduction is the lower body's best strategy for stability and support.

Warrior Two

Folded straddle

The Back

We are creatures that look forward, move forward, and think forward. Most people confine their external awareness to a five foot perimeter from the front of their bodies. What goes on behind us normally passes unnoticed. How many times have you bumped your backside up against a wall because you misjudged its proximity? Have you ever stepped backwards onto another person because you were unaware of their presence?

A substantial portion of whom and what we are is based on our past. This is symbolized by the awareness in our backs. Our backs also contribute to our future by representing intuitive perception that can sense forthcoming encounters. A strong yet flexible back embodies the ability to confront the unknown. It provides the security and confidence of a well-developed support system.

❖ Inquiry # 11: "Back breathing"

Concept: In this inquiry, we seek to experience the sensation of bringing the breath into the back.

Discussion: Child's pose is an extremely comfortable and comforting position for the back, because it helps the back to relax and release.

Directions: To assume the child's pose, sit on your heels and fold forward from the hips. Place your forehead on the floor. Your arms may be folded by your sides with the palms facing up, or they may extend forward on the floor alongside your head with the palms facing down. Relax in this position for a few moments and breathe comfortably.

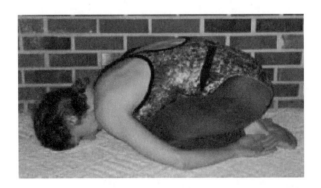

Inquiry # 11: "Back breathing" (child's pose)

Bring your attention to your back. Notice its length and width. Visualize the back as containing four separate chambers – an upper right, an upper left, a lower right, and a lower left. Begin by consciously directing the breath into the lower right chamber. Breathe into and out of this area. Then consciously direct the breath into the lower left chamber. Breathe into and out of this area. Consciously direct the breath into the upper right chamber, breathing there. Finally, direct the breath into the upper left chamber, breathing there.

As you go through this breathing inquiry, be sure to sense the movement of the breath in each chamber separately, noting which areas breathe more easily and naturally, and which areas feel more constricted. Then breathe into the whole right side (upper and lower chambers on the right), and into the whole left side (upper and lower chambers on the left). Finally, breathe into and out of the back-as-a-whole.

Sexual Parts

Yoga instructors and yoga texts make few, if any, references to the possibility of experiencing a somatic awakening in the body's sexual parts. Though generally unmentioned and subliminally taboo, sensations of sexual stimulation do arise during yoga asana.

Repressed emotions and traumatic experiences associated with one's sexuality can cause certain body parts to be unresponsive or numb. This dormancy in somatic awareness is called sensori-motor amnesia (and it is not confined to the body's sexual parts). Amnesic body parts have lost their conscious connection to the mind. Fortunately, sensori-motor amnesia need not be an irreversible condition. Yoga asana returns somatic sensation to amnesic parts by consciously acknowledging their existence. Instead of rejecting these body parts, asana challenges us to accept and ratify the body-as-a-whole.

❖ Inquiry # 12: "Straddle stance"

Concept: In this inquiry, we acknowledge the existence of the body's sexual parts.

Discussion: The standing straddle stance makes everyone feel somewhat uncorked. It's hard to ignore the unsettling feeling of having your legs spread apart. In this wide-open position, our personal parts feel unprotected and accessible. Most students say that the straddle pose is rather unnatural and uncomfortable. Some say it provokes somatic sensations that are alarming and embarrassing. This pose is notorious for exposing hidden or unresolved psychological issues of vulnerability. Students have reported a sense of freedom, losing control, undirected energy, or guilty pleasure.

Inquiry # 12: "Straddle stance"

Directions: Take a wide stance, about three feet apart. The legs are straight but not locked straight. Keep the feet parallel. Roll the shoulders down your back, and extend the neck so the crown of the head rises up. Direct the tailbone gently downward to create a full extension of the spinal column from top to bottom.

Bring your attention to the slow, steady breath. Every time your exhale, let your body relax a little more. Close your eyes and transfer your attention to the location and sensation of the spinal column. In your mind's eye, this image should extend all the way up and out through the crown of the head. Likewise, it should drop all the way down and out through the perineum. Focus on the open and unobstructed nature of the body's central channel. Let yourself continue to relax so that you can appreciate the powerful sensation of an open and unobstructed center.

As we start to contemplate the use of our eyes, jaw, feet, legs, and lower body, these parts become more real to us. By directing our attention to the forgotten parts, they come alive. They make us aware of their participation in the life of the soma. We gain an appreciation for how each of these parts contributes to the body-as-a-whole. As we contact our forgotten parts, they respond by enlivening us!

CHAPTER SIX

The Center

In a room filled with yoga students, the instructor calls out "Center your self before we move on." Everyone immediately brings their hands together in prayer gesture at the center of the chest. They close their eyes. Standing perfectly still, they take a deep calming breath – just as they have been taught to. Is that it? Are these students centered?

For the onlooker, it's hard to tell. Being centered is not necessarily something one can observe. The centered experience is as much mental as it is physical. It represents a particular state of being based on internal mental and physical sensations. This state can be accurately assessed only by our own internal connection to sensory awareness. It is dependant upon how well we truly know and recognize our habitual mental and physical states of being.

There are certain standard observable clues that indicate the manifestation of the centered state. We can learn to recognize such clues in ourselves and in others. These clues include freedom of movement in the thorax, abdomen, and back when breathing. A relaxed brow and jaw, shoulders that are not hunched up to the ears, toes that do not curl under, and hands that are not clenched also indicate a relaxed, centered state.

When we are centered, we have no apparent need to hurry or rush. We display a serene and joyful demeanor, an accepting, non-judgmental nature, and an inquisitive willingness. The centered state contains no indication of anger, offensive behavior, critical or condescending thoughts, or impure intentions.

The root word 'center' provides a tangible description of the centered state. The center is a point equidistant from all points on the boundaries. It is the point that is exactly in the middle, around which everything revolves. The center serves as the focal point of activity and influence. The implication is that this middle point is in conscious contact with all points external to it.

When we are centered we sense that our consciousness is located deep within the body. At the same time we have awareness of all the surrounding body parts and their relationship or connection to the middle. Think of the center as your home base, and remember that *all roads lead home*. Esoterically, the center is associated with the spirit, the soul, and the essence of consciousness. It represents your highest authority.

The centered individual relies on information provided by the five senses as well as information accessed by the sixth sense. He understands that appearances can be deceiving, and that the truth is often buried deep inside. He trusts the wisdom and guidance of intuition. Other qualities associated with the centered experience include operating from the core, preparation, moderation, being present, peace and tranquility, and connection.

➢ Operating from the core

Centered feels like you are operating from a deep position of safety and understanding. This position is located at the core of your being. From the security of such a central location, you can comfortably expand outward in any direction. This is just like a well-adjusted child who has grown up in a loving, secure home environment. Such an environment supports and encourages activities like seeking, learning, and integrating. This child loves to explore and participate in the world around her. She views the world as a beautiful, safe, and inviting place where she can grow.

When this child is affronted, she is not easily vanquished. She understands that encountering polarity is a natural part of the life process. Unfortunately, not everyone is raised in an environment that fosters a natural tendency toward the centered state of being. Many of us have had to learn or relearn existence from a centered state.

➢ Preparation

Perhaps you have heard meditation described as awareness of all points at the same time. Centered is a similar concept, but it is usually employed in a preparatory context. It implies both physical and psychological preparation that is characterized by emotional stability and equilibrium. Being centered could be described as a neutral state which one prepares to venture. It declares no particular intention or expectation. It involves a state of peaceful readiness. It is that middle ground from which we begin our journey or departure. And it is the place we return to when coming back home to one's self.

➢ Moderation

When we are centered, even virtue and vice are rendered null and void. There are no hard boundaries or extreme limitations. In this moderate state, fluidity and the ability to adapt are the norm. The centered approach embraces the unification mentality of *sharing, becoming ours.*

The opposite of being centered is being guarded. The guarded approach is characterized by the separation mentality of *mine, not yours.* The guarded individual has the need to patrol and protect. People who are guarded identify solely with the body as self. They tend to be obsessed with how things look. They prefer a lifestyle based on control, habituation, and status quo. By shunting any form of possibility thinking, they firmly establish their own version of reality.

> Being present

Perhaps what is meant by being centered can be expressed best in familiar phrases like being in-the-moment, flowing with the feeling, in tune with synchronicity, and resting in that peaceful, easy feeling. The centered state embraces the free flow of feelings and sensations. It is not a predetermined event. Instead, it is a moment to moment re-assessment of one's internal state of being. Mindfulness is another term commonly used to express this type of awareness.

> Peace and tranquility

Being centered indicates a state of attunement that lets you move through life with equanimity. This is a desirable state because it is peaceful. Psychologically, when we are centered, we are in control of our responses. We are calm and tranquil. We feel that we can manage.

The centered individual operates from an internal locus of control. Emotionally, when we are centered we are not afraid. When we are not afraid, we can afford to be magnanimous. Like the well-nurtured child, we perceive the world as a safe, supportive place in which we can interact, assist, learn, and grow.

> Connection

Sensing connections within our own bodies make us feel whole. These inner connections are a metaphor for a much larger, grander connection. When we are centered, we consciously contact the serenity of unity.

Trace it to the Core

Finding and experiencing the body's center means making mental contact with the physical sensations at the body's core. This area is commonly referred to as the body's center of gravity. The following simple meditative experiences encourage this conscious connection. Each inquiry is designed to yield a mental connection with awareness of the body's physical center. The key question for contemplation in these inquiries is *"Where does the experience begin in the body? Trace it to the core."*

❖ Inquiry # 13a: "Make a fist"

Concept: This inquiry shows how tension in the extremities creates tension in the core. It also reinforces the fact that body parts are interrelated. The lesson is that what we experience in one body part is, to a certain extent, also experienced by the body as a whole.

Directions: Lying in savasana (the corpse pose), make a fist with one hand. Squeeze the fingers as tightly as you can. Notice the sensation of tension in the fingers, the hand, and up into the forearm. Then notice how accessory musculature participates in the tense state, whether specifically directed to or not.

Inquiry # 13a: "Make a fist"

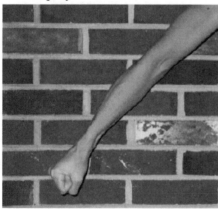

Follow the trail of the tension up the arm toward the shoulder. Is the shoulder tense or tight? Keep squeezing the fist and keep following the path of tension further into the body.

Notice that even though the contraction seems to be most intense at the point of origin (the fist), the tension is not limited to that location. It gradually spreads deeper, making its way to the core. As you continue squeezing the fist, try to locate exactly how far the tension has traveled in your body. *Where does the tension begin in the body? Trace it to the core.*

❖ Inquiry # 13b: "Depressed stance"

Concept: Our mental and emotional states have a direct effect on our bodies. In this inquiry, we study the manifestation of depression in the physical body.

Discussion: We can tell if a person is depressed simply by looking at him. Stereotypically depressed posture includes a hanging head, rounded and droopy shoulders, and an unsteady, shuffling gait. Facial features seem to sag, lacking vibrancy or support.

Inquiry # 13b:
"Depressed stance"

Directions: To perform this inquiry, inhale deeply. Then whoosh all the air out while letting the head and shoulders (or the whole torso) collapse forward. Make a big sigh and let your body hang like a rag doll. With the body folded in this position, contemplate questions like "How does this body position make me feel? What is the emotion associated with this body position? *Where does the perception begin in the body? Trace it to the core.*

If you verbalize or journal your findings, the precision of your response could surprise you. You might say something like "I feel like I have given up. I feel like I have nothing left. I feel tired and beaten. I don't care. I'm worn out." Notice how the verbal summations arose from physical sensations. Notice that the summations clearly indicate mental depression. The lesson is that the physical affects the mental and vice versa. Both aspects touch the core of our being and affect us deeply.

❖ Inquiry # 13c: "Forward fold with pulsation"

Concept: In this inquiry, we are introduced to the concept that all physical action originates in the body's core.

Directions: Perform the standing forward fold pose with the fingers or hands touching the floor. Knees may be slightly bent. Create a tiny pulsing action, as if repeatedly pressing the crown of the head toward the floor. Try to identify *where the movement originates in the body. Trace it to the core.* If you are able to trace the sensation all the way back to the source of the impulse, you will come to the conclusion that the action originates deep within the pelvis - in the body's center of gravity.

Inquiry # 13c:
"Forward fold with pulsation"

In this inquiry we are peeling back the layers of protective tension in an attempt to reach the center of our being. If we encounter habitual tension, it stops us in our tracks. We recognize it immediately because it holds us back. We're blocked from going further. Extremely tight hamstrings are an example of habitual tension. Tight hamstrings won't accommodate the complete forward fold position. In this case, our awareness is captured by the screaming sensation in the legs. Confined to this limitation, we never make the connection to the core.

Eventually we discover that the original impulse for movement begins in the body's center. With this discovery, we become more aware of our potentialities and possibilities. At the same time, we become less aware of our boundaries (boundaries being 'what I am' vs. 'what I am not'). We are often surprised at the expansive feeling of the centered self. This expansive self is most accurately defined by its ability for empathetic connection. This connection, when it finally occurs, is both welcome and well deserved.

The Centering Activity

A centering activity is an integral part of any mind-body methods class. Initially, it acts as a call to attention. It is an invitation to leave your problems at the door. It is an opportunity to temporarily relinquish interest in the distractions of everyday life. The centering activity provides a comfortable ritual that builds structure and encourages familiarity. It allows a brief period of mental and physical preparation. It is a time to renew the bond of the group as a whole. It also provides a time to re-connect with the continuing commitment toward a common cause.

Types of centering activities vary. They are often quite simple and brief. But they can also be pretentious or profound. Some yoga instructors will have the students stand quietly and sense their breathing. Many instructors use the Sun Salutation as a centering activity. Others begin with a formal chant or a spiritual song. The students may listen or sing along.

Whether you attend a class or practice yoga by yourself at home, you should recognize the importance of what it means to be centered. Include some sort of centering activity in your daily practice. A basic, non-denominational centering activity fosters respect for the teachings and tradition of yoga. It honors the student as a responsible individual who willingly chooses to participate in this program for the purpose of self-improvement.

Consider our initial yoga class scenario. Whether these students are centered or not, they have made a good attempt! Let's look at the effects of their centering ritual.

✓ *Being still* turns our attention inward. This allows us to monitor ourselves via the somatic sensations of our internal environment (the body).

✓ *Closing the eyes* shuts out external (visual) distractions.

✓ *Bringing the hands together in prayer gesture at the heart* promotes unity within the self via connection of the arms and hands. Symbolically, arms and hands represent our vehicle for reaching out to interact with the world around us. This gesture redirects outward-flowing energy back into the heart center.

✓ *Taking a deep, calming breath* goes a long way toward steadying all aspects of the self by physically calming down and mentally refocusing. Regulating the breath is generally considered the quickest and easiest way to reduce stress and restore homeostasis.

Enlighten Your Body

CHAPTER SEVEN

The Psoas

Enhanced somatic awareness lets us access biofeedback that was previously beyond the scope of our normal consciousness. We gradually become more aware of the internal movements and sensations that arise from deep within the body's core. We might begin to notice fluctuations in our heart rate, our tension level, our respiration, our digestion, and even our bones.

The concept of the 'center' contributes to the process of consciously connecting with our internal environment. Specifically, the psycho-somatic nature of the 'centered state' includes a growing awareness of the body's core musculature. This key muscle is called the psoas. Just as many of us find the centered state to be elusive or fleeting, many of us haven't an inkling as to the existence of the psoas muscle.

The psoas is the deepest and largest core muscle of the body, extending up to fifteen inches in length. Its superior attachments are at T-12 and the five lumbar vertebrae. Its lower insertion occurs at the lesser trochanter of each femur. When you think of the psoas, think of connections. The psoas connects the upper and lower portions of the body by bridging the trunk to each leg. It also connects the body's front and back sides.

Most people aren't aware that the psoas is quite possibly one of the most essential yet controversial muscles in the body. Anatomical theorists continue to debate the role of the psoas. Most theorists believe that the psoas is the primary hip flexor. But there are a few who say that it *extends* the hip. Some propose that irregularities of the psoas muscle are the primary cause of functional scoliosis. Others contend that the psoas should not be indicted in this anatomical misalignment.

While researching material for a fitness course, I studied everything I could find about the psoas. When I finished the project, I was still somewhat confused about this enigmatic muscle. But there was one thing I was sure of. I was certain that my psoas had a problem!

I've suffered most of my life with back pain from scoliosis. The doctors called it 'minor.' They said as long as I wasn't incapacitated, I shouldn't pursue any invasive treatments for correcting my spinal curvature. So I suffered with mild to moderate backaches everyday for about twenty years. I resigned myself to the fact that I would be a yoga teacher with an aching back. But sometimes, somewhere in my mind, I wondered if I could get fixed. Maybe I was chasing a rainbow, but I began to wonder if it might be possible to change the structure of my spine.

I kept thinking about what I had learned from my research on the psoas muscle. In functional scoliosis, the curvature of the spine is not produced by misshapen vertebrae. The curvature is created by a functional incapacity. This means that it is caused by an irregular use of the *musculature*. My gut instinct was telling me that the psoas played a main role in my backaches and my scoliosis. If this were the case, there was a good chance that my problem could be corrected!

One of my first real moments of hope came when I started riding bikes with my kids. I was about forty years old. As I pedaled through the neighborhood, I noticed that the left side of my body made a weird twisting motion. Every time I pushed down on the left pedal, the left side of my back jerked involuntarily. It was like a tiny internal spasm. My right side didn't do that. By keeping my back very still and straight as my legs cycled, I could control the left side's tendency to twist. And the weak musculature of the left hip was forced to engage.

What a strange feeling! My left hip and left leg quickly became very fatigued. I could tell that I was forcing lethargic muscles to wake up and get to work. Unbeknownst to me, they'd been asleep on the job for *many* years.

After a few months of rehabilitative cycling, I began to notice something else that I had never felt before. Something was moving deep inside my body. Every time I pedaled with the left leg, there was a fluttering feeling up under my lowest rib. It was some sort of activation at the core! For the first time, I was feeling the psoas muscle at work.

To make a long story short, I labored hard for about two years to strengthen, stretch, release, and rehabilitate the psoas muscle. This reconstruction program also addressed my pelvic obliquity. To straighten the pelvis, I had to learn how to walk all over again. Through trial and error, I literally taught my body the right way to walk.

My scoliosis and daily backaches have, for the most part, almost totally disappeared. As a result of my own healing experience, I believe that the psoas plays a key role in functional scoliosis. Irregular use of the psoas might not be the only cause of scoliosis, but it is certainly one of them. I am convinced that the condition of the psoas muscle has a direct effect on many other muscles in the body.

When the psoas is out of whack, muscles in the hip, thigh, and back will also be out of whack. Most likely the use of at least one leg and foot will have gone awry. To restore proper functioning of the psoas, all of the associated muscles and body parts need to be addressed. This is not particularly easy, and it does not occur quickly. Because of its key function as our deepest, most basic bodily connection, it's worthwhile getting to know more about the psoas.

Understanding the role played by the psoas muscle is difficult, partly because the muscle itself is hidden deep within the body. It cannot be easily palpitated or observed. Despite controversy over the psoas' specific function, all anatomical experts affirm the psoas muscle's crucial role in obtaining optimal vertical posture. The psoas also provides the best mechanical advantage during ambulation (walking). Due to its proximal anatomical location to the base of the diaphragm, it even facilitates proper respiration

A pliable psoas is an asset to one's functional capacity and general health. A well-toned psoas allows natural, unrestricted movement in the body's midsection. At the same time, it helps us feel grounded, safe, and secure. The sensations of freedom and security in the body's core coincide with a sense of harmony and magnanimity. Good mobility in the pelvis and an absence of back pain are the best indications of a healthy, well-functioning psoas.

Without a healthy, functional psoas, the body is not supported by adequate core strength. The inner thighs, abdomen, and lower back will lack strength and tone. To compensate for these weaknesses, the neck, shoulders, buttocks, and outer thighs must bear habitual tension. A body struggling with a weak psoas is literally propped up by its superficial musculature.

The health of the psoas is distinctly affected by our physical patterns of use. Interestingly enough, it is also affected by our characteristic psychological nature. Symbolically, a healthy psoas represents our ability to access knowledge via intuition. On a physical level, it indicates a conscious connection to our core.

A malfunctioning psoas limits our ability to live in a comfortable, healthy body. Problems with the psoas are often due to stress. If we are frequently on guard or under stress, the psoas reflects this tension. As one of the flexor muscles, the psoas participates in the startle reflex. When threatened, the body compresses the core musculature as a means of self-preservation. If we suffer from repeated demands for the startle reflex or the fear response, the body will eventually become locked in a distorted posture.

We usually don't recognize the somatic sensation of an anxious psoas. Unlike a frozen shoulder that is easily identified by its elevated position, a frozen psoas presents no overt symptoms. Indications of a rigid, non-functional psoas are so subtle that they are typically overlooked or misdiagnosed. Minute adaptations in functional capacity or barely noticeable holding patterns are often the first signs of core compression. Later symptoms include reduced pelvic mobility, choppy breathing, ankle or knee pain, a sore neck, or poor elimination. Obviously, none of these symptoms would make us suspect a problem in the psoas.

It has been my experience that most people's psoas muscle suffers from some degree of dysfunction. Common indications of a weak psoas include the following:

✓ You cannot sit upright in a cross-legged position without complaining of backache.
✓ Your feet are extremely turned out while standing and walking.
✓ You tend toward eversion. This is known as 'rolling out' or bearing weight on the outer edge of the foot.
✓ You cannot sit comfortably on a chair with your feet flat on the floor in front of you.

Our most prudent approach for rehabilitating this important muscle is to use a balanced program that will stretch and strengthen the psoas. We probably need to start with restorative positions that encourage a habitually tight psoas to gradually release.

❖ Inquiry # 14: "Psoas Rehab"

Concept: This inquiry consists of asanas and exercises for psoas release, stretching, and strengthening.

❖ Inquiry # 14a: "Release"

To get the psoas to release, you need to remain in the position for an extended period of time. It might take as much as 20 minutes to yield optimal results. The idea is to relax the body-as-a-whole. Along with a little help from gravity, your body will finally relax deep inside. This is a passive re-training program. We want to gently encourage a frozen psoas to remember how to relax. Try any or all of these three release positions.

(1) Supine rest pose with legs bend at 45 degree angle

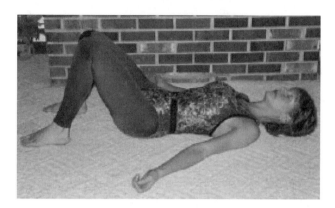

Inquiry #14a: "Release"

Directions: Place the feet flat on the floor, positioned at a comfortable distance away from the buttocks. Allow the knees to tip inward against each other. You shouldn't feel the need to hold the legs in place. Close your eyes and relax. With each exhalation, mentally repeat the affirmation "Let go."

(2) Single leg supine rest position: one leg resting at a 90 degree angle on bench

Inquiry #14a: "Release"

Directions: Use a bench or chair of appropriate height so that the leg can be positioned with the knee directly above the hip. The lower part of the leg is supported as it rests horizontally on the bench. Gradually feel the release in the lower back and both hips. The release is successful when you no longer feel that you are gripping or holding the bent leg.

(3) Supine rest position: both legs resting at a 90 degree angle on bench

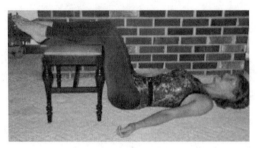

Inquiry # 14a: "Release"

Directions: This pose is just like the previous one, except that both lower legs rest on the bench. These release poses are meant to be held for extended periods of time to allow the opportunity to wind down both mentally and physically. The intent is to let go and experience relief from deep internal compression.

❖ Inquiry # 14b: "Stretch"

A tight, weak psoas will limit the range of motion during leg lifts. Conversely, a well-toned psoas will easily accommodate femoral flexion as in the ballet dancer's grande battement kicks. To restore proper resting length and pliability to the psoas, try these two stretch-positions.

(1) Lunge pose

Inquiry # 14b: "Stretch"

Directions: Position the right knee directly above the right ankle. Move the left knee as far back on the floor as possible, while maintaining the right leg's vertical knee-to-ankle alignment. Sink the pelvis. Ease the breastbone forward. Keep the head and neck neutral. Gaze forward at eye level. Finger tips on the floor alongside your hips will provide additional support. Remain in the position for 1-2 minutes. Then do the other side.

(2) Pigeon pose

Inquiry
14b:
"Stretch"

Directions: From a seated position with the buttocks resting on the heels, shift the body's weight onto the right heel. Extend the left leg straight back. Shift the right hip further to the right and lower it down. Though the hip might not rest on the floor, the pelvis should be positioned behind the shin of the folded leg. Keep the front heel proximal to the opposite frontal hip bone. The hips are squared, facing forward. Do not twist or overarch the lower back. If necessary, lean the torso forward slightly. Support the body's weight on the hands. Be still for 1-2 minutes. Do the other side.

❖ Inquiry # 14c: "Strength"

If you want to strengthen the psoas, old fashioned sit-ups and straight leg raises performed in a supine position will definitely do the trick. Be aware that both of these exercises are contraindicated for certain populations. For this reason, many fitness instructors omit these movements from their repertoire.

(1) Seated cobbler pose

Directions: Sit up on the sitz bones and place the soles of the feet together on the floor in front of you. Hold onto the ankles and sit tall. Keep the spine erect. Pull the navel inward and downward toward your tailbone. Gently allow the knees to open away from each other.

Inquiry # 14c: "Strength"

71

Inquiry # 14c: "Strength"

(2) Seated
straddle
pose

Directions: Sit on the sitz bones with the legs extended apart. Pull the spinal column upright. The main idea is to maintain a neutral pelvis, but to relax the body's weight down into the sitz bones.

(3) Single leg lifts performed in a supine position

Directions: In a supine position, bend the left leg and place the foot flat on the floor. This position will allow the pelvis and lower back to remain stable. The right leg is extended straight on the floor. This leg lifts and lowers smoothly, and in coordination with the breath. Inhale as the leg rises. Exhale as the leg descends. Keep the foot pointed as the leg rises. Switch to a flexed foot (the heel leads) going down. Be sure to press the back of the waist and the non-working foot into the floor for stability.

Inquiry # 14c:
"Strength"

To encourage active participation of the psoas, visualize a sweeping force coming from under the buttocks and behind the thigh. Use this 'scooping upward from underneath' image to create the lift, instead of tightening and bunching up in the abdomen or overworking the rectus femoris of the thigh. (We want to target the psoas, not the abdomen or the thigh).

Be sure to allow a hollowing or softening in the abdomen during the leg lift portion of the exercise. Start with 10 steady repetitions on each leg and gradually work up to 20. Emphasize good form. Then change legs and do the other side.

(4) Leg swings performed in a standing position

Directions: When learning this movement, it helps to stand alongside a wall for balance. Stand on the inside foot, nearest the wall. Let the outside leg swing freely forward and back. Keep the torso as vertical as possible, but you needn't force this position. Start with a small range of motion. If you are able, gradually increase up to 90 degree forward flexion from the hip. The backward motion should go no higher than 45 degrees, or it can be omitted altogether.

Inquiry
14c:
"Strength"

(5) Classic sit-up

Directions: Begin in a supine position with the arms extended over your head. Your legs may be fully extended or the feet can be placed flat

on the floor. Before you begin, inhale deeply. As you exhale, curl the head and torso up and over the legs. Let the finger tips reach toward the knees or the toes. Initially this action will be accomplished by the momentum of throwing the arms upward and forward. As core strength improves, the movement will be smooth and controlled.

Inquiry # 14c: "Strength"

Enlighten Your Body

CHAPTER EIGHT

The Edge

I've never been the kind of person who lives on the edge. My husband and my children call me the chicken of the family. In the past, I have had more than my fair share of fears. Sometimes it seems like I've experienced every single fear that humankind has ever known.

I don't like heights. I don't like deep water or pitch darkness. I don't like unstable surfaces such as gravel or sand or ice. I don't like driving on slick roads. I no longer see scary movies, and I'm still afraid of spiders and snakes. I am one of those people who ask about safety. I prefer to look before I leap. Having said all this, I can assure you that I'm much braver than I used to be. I'm no longer instantly afraid of confronting my 'edge.'

The first big lesson I got in 'living on the edge' was the snorkeling expedition on my honeymoon. The Hawaiian crew of this cute little tourist boat was passing out snorkel gear to anyone who wanted to participate. David was one of the first to get into the water. Of course I would be one of the few who stayed onboard. One by one people plopped into the ocean and began paddling around. I noticed that most people weren't very good at snorkeling, but they managed.

Then I saw her. She was a very old, very small, very emaciated Japanese grandmother that could barely walk. Maybe she was a great grandmother. She had to be a hundred years old. At most she weighed eighty-five pounds. I watched as family members hoisted her frail body over the side of the boat.

This decrepit old woman was going snorkeling? What were they thinking? Yet there she was – clinging to the surfboard and struggling to keep herself afloat. Somehow she paddled around in the big ocean, dunking her face and looking for fish.

I was shamed into doing it. I pulled on those heavy black flippers and that horrible stinky rubber face mask. I grabbed a surfboard and plopped into the ocean. It still took a few moments for David to convince me to put my face in the water. But when I did, Wow! There was an amazing new world under the sea! I discovered that I loved snorkeling.

I would have missed this incredible experience if I hadn't been willing to go to the edge and face my fear. I realized that the world wasn't going to stop just because I was afraid to do something. I understood that being afraid could make me miss opportunities. I also noticed that other people's edges seemed much further back than mine. These illuminating insights made me question and confront my well-defined limitations.

One of my worst fears is, quite literally, the edge. I don't like cliffs. Yet there are plenty of people who love the challenge of scaling a cliff just so they can stand at the top and look down. Unfortunately for me, my husband and my kids are that kind of person. They took one look at the beautiful red rock formations in Sedona, Arizona and immediately turned into wild mountain goats! They simply had to get to the top of the nearest cliff.

While they climbed, I waited at the bottom. I whacked mosquitoes and pointed out the trail markers to other hikers. I tried hard not to notice that my family was clambering along the top of Coffeepot rock. Didn't they know that they were on the edge of a cliff? What were they thinking? To them, this edge was not a problem.

The hardest (and certainly the highest) edge I've ever faced was when David and I visited the Angkor Wat Temple in Cambodia. We were both really excited to see this place. On the bus drive from the hotel, our tour guide announced that he would take us through the first and second levels of the temple. But if we wanted to see the third level, we were on our own. He said that he wasn't going to risk his life by making the steep climb to the top. Of course, the top sanctuary is the spiritual heart of the Temple. Having traveled half way around the world to see this, David and I planned on (gulp) going to the top.

We made our way through the winding corridors on the first and second levels and finally came to a central courtyard. "There it is," David cried, pointing to the high tower in the middle of this huge stone courtyard. He started running toward it. Without looking back he reached up and started climbing.

At first I was right behind him. But when I was about eight feet off the ground, I stopped dead in my tracks. This wasn't really an ancient staircase. This was more like a vertical stone ladder. The extremely steep, sand-covered steps were only four inches wide and well worn. This was like climbing forty feet up the side of a cliff!

My fingertips kept sliding as I struggled to pull myself up, and I couldn't get a good foothold on the narrow slippery steps! I was worried that the weight of my backpack was going to pull me over backwards. "I can't do this," I shouted to David. "Don't look down," was his advice.

Somehow I made it to the top. David pulled me up into the safety of the corner turret. My body and mind were in the midst of a major emergency response. My eyes were big and wild. My heart was pumping like it had never pumped before. I saw nothing but at the same time I saw everything. "We're at the top of Angkor Wat!" David cheered.

I had no reason to celebrate. I was already terrorized by the thought of climbing back down. For a moment, I considered becoming a monk and staying at the top of the Temple for the rest of my life. Realistically, that was not a good option. Sooner or later, I was going to have to face those very steep steps.

For the next twenty minutes, we toured the third level. I remained in shock but reminded myself to keep breathing. As we prepared to descend, I stood right at the edge and looked down. I thought about the other people who had done it. I thought to myself, "If they can, maybe I can too." I saw that everyone was scared, just like me. I could see that most people were even more scared than I was. In a strange way, seeing others so scared was comforting. I started to calm down. I relaxed and knew I could do it. We made it down safely.

The edge is the path that leads us to new horizons. Sure, it can be more than a little bit scary and uncomfortable. But the edge isn't something to be desperately afraid of. It's just the place between familiar and unfamiliar territory. It's the place or the moment that offers a curious mixture of discomfort and discovery.

The Edge in Yoga

During asana practice, we are often told to "find your edge" or "approach your edge" in the pose. What exactly is the edge? Possibly the best indicator of what our bodies need is found in the concept called the 'edge.' The edge is that dividing line between pushing too hard and not trying hard enough. The edge represents the present boundaries of our comfort zone. It is a somatic representation of the point at which we are unsure of what lies beyond.

In the dictionary, the edge is most commonly defined as the degree of sharpness, keenness or zest. It can refer to a rim, crest, or ridge – being at the top or outermost position. It can be a dividing line, a point of transition, or a border. It can indicate a margin of superiority or an advantage. And it can suggest eager anticipation or impatience. To be "on edge" means to have an unpleasant reaction or feelings of nervousness and irritability. To "edge forward" is to advance or push onward gradually and in a hesitant manner.

From these definitions, we can identify five features regarding the concept of the edge. These features include (1) placement, (2) approaching the potential for change or approaching the unknown, (3) attitude or opinion, (4) gradual movement coupled with conscious awareness, and (5) intensity.

First, the edge implies placement. The edge is a particular place, location, or position. Both physically and psychologically, the edge indicates placement inside one's comfort zone. But this placement approaches the boundaries of comfort, confidence, and familiarity.

The edge suggests that if we pass beyond a certain placement, change will undoubtedly occur. 'Going to the edge' acknowledges the potential for change by cautiously approaching the unknown. Moving onward into new, unknown territory is a risky venture. As the familiar is left behind, so is the feeling of comfort. We might experience anxiety, fear, or unsettledness.

Esoterically, being at one's edge is like walking a line between growth and resistance to change. On one side lies rigidity and crystallization of present tendencies, beliefs, and self-defining patterns. This is the side marked status quo. Though this side might be less than satisfactory, at least it is comfortable. It is fairly safe, familiar, and manageable. On the other side lies unexplored territory that is rich with possibilities. This is the path of uncertainty regarding your potential and your future. Crossing over to this side, you actively challenge your current boundaries and limitations.

The edge implies attitude or opinion. This attitude is characterized by irrepressible qualities which demand one's attention. These qualities can have a positive ('keenness' or 'zest'), negative ('nervous' or 'irritable'), or mixed ('sharpness' or 'anticipated') manifestation. The edge also conveys a sense of doing one's best ('margin of superiority' or 'advantage'), as well as comparison to others.

Used as an action word, edge suggests a form of movement or approach that is performed carefully. We 'edge forward' in a slow, gradual, and hesitant manner. Careful, gradual movement is necessary due to the element of inherent risk Working safely at your edge requires the ability to make minute adjustments that are almost undetectable. This is extremely technical work based on patience, vigilance, precision of execution, and continual re-evaluation. Any misjudgment or risky, random behavior could result in pain or injury. Being on the edge always carries with it the possibility of slipping off, falling down, or failure.

The edge implies intensity. The edge in asana occurs in that moment or placement when the intensity is almost painful. The ability to locate and remain at your limit of manageable intensity in a pose is a significant feature of the asana experience. This is a personal challenge that the individual creates and accepts. Working safely in this situation demands your total attention, intuition, and wisdom to guide you. This challenge is precisely what the asana experience is all about.

Honor thy Body

Stillness and silence in the pose help us focus on the internal environment of the body. In this way, we begin to hear the subtle messages that our bodies are constantly sending us. These messages register in our consciousness as sensations and emotions. As we tune in to these messages, we notice that they change everyday. Some days our bodies feel well rested, healthy, and able. On those days we feel that asana is easy.

Other times our bodies feel stiff, sore, or tired, and every pose seems difficult. By listening to somatic feedback from our bodies, we can choose the appropriate focus for the daily practice. Doing what is appropriate instead of sticking to a pre-arranged agenda is an intelligent and safe way to practice. It is a way of honoring the body. If we listen, the body will tell us exactly what it needs.

❖ Inquiry # 15a: "Staying still"

Concept: In this inquiry, we experience the edge by confronting the dimension of time. Our challenge is to hold the pose much longer than usual. This will be very different from performing a pose briefly, as in most yoga classes. It is more difficult because you cannot randomly decide to quit when your muscles become fatigued. The factor of necessary *duration* greatly amplifies the degree of difficulty. *Be sure to notice your psychological reaction as well.

Directions: You will perform this inquiry two times. The first time you will perform the easier child's pose. The second time you will perform the more difficult diver pose. Have someone time you in each pose, or set an alarm. If you are a beginner, set the alarm for three minutes. More accomplished students may use five minutes. It is imperative that you do not look at the clock while performing this inquiry. Allow yourself to have the experience of duration and perseverance in the pose without 'checking in' to see how much time has passed or how much time is left. Peeking at the clock is just a way of distracting yourself from your true purpose in this inquiry. It is a psychological escape strategy for avoiding the pressures and inconveniences associated with managing the challenge of an unknown variable. (This inquiry could also be placed under time management in Chapter 13.)

Inquiry # 15a: "Staying still"

child's pose

diver pose

❖ Inquiry # 15b: "Seated straddle"

Concept: In this inquiry, we approach the edge by gradually increasing the intensity of the stretch sensation. We also learn to choose an appropriate and manageable amount of physical challenge in the pose.

Inquiry # 15b: "Seated straddle"

Directions: To perform the inquiry, begin by sitting in what you consider to be a manageable straddle position. For most people, this is already a very challenging proposition!

Place your hands on the floor just behind your hips. Push down with the hands and lift your pelvis off the floor, moving it forward one inch. Lower the pelvis to the floor and rest. Notice the increased stretch sensation at the inner thighs. When comfort is re-established in this new position, go through the procedure again. Lift your pelvis, move it forward one inch, and lower down. Again notice the increased intensity.

Do you feel any resistance in the form of mental or physical doubts? Rest for a moment, and then reassess. Do you think that you can possibly move forward one more time? If so, go for it. If not, stay where you are and continue to breathe steadily as you try to re-establish bodily comfort and equilibrium in the pose. To move out of the straddle position, slowly close the legs together.

Control or Surrender?

Think of the edge as your present limit or established personal boundary. When undertaking the yoga challenge, you attempt to gradually, carefully, and consciously push back or remove the limit. As you extend or stretch your outer boundaries in the pose, you notice corresponding changes in the parameters of inner thought patterns as well. You realize that you have the power and responsibility to choose your thoughts and your responses. Depending on the appropriate choice, you can either succeed by control or by surrender. The edge teaches you to find the proper balance between control and surrender.

There are two basic personality types in yoga. Each addresses the challenge of meeting one's edge in a different manner. As a result, each needs to learn a different lesson to become successful, balanced, and whole. The two types are the Achievers and the Quiescents. Achievers are those people that desire control, progress, and discipline. The Achiever needs to learn how to surrender, detach, and let go. Quiescents prefer inactivity, status quo, and dormancy. The Quiescent needs to learn how to get motivated, get moving, and generate energy.

Once you identify which of these personality types is predominant, your transformation begins. With delight, you observe and participate in the creation of your own evolution. Soon you no longer immediately and habitually say to yourself "This is as far as I can go" (Quiescent).

When faced with any demanding pose, difficult situation, or personal challenge, you won't automatically default into give-up mode (Quiescent). Nor will you be bored with poses that you have already mastered (Achiever). You won't feel defeated if you cannot outperform all other students by executing the hardest or most challenging pose (Achiever). And you will still feel good about yourself even when it is clear that you are no longer the cutest, youngest, strongest, or smartest.

Learn to think in terms of possibilities, such as "Let me see what I can do today. Let me try, for I might be able. Let me try, for I think I can." This is the can-do attitude. This attitude implies moderation and openness to change. It also implies non-rigidity in the body and non-fixation in the mind. If signifies a new willingness to continually improve the self through mind-body awareness.

Both the body and the mind have great flexibility for forming and reforming themselves. We can choose to recreate ourselves appropriately under any circumstance. We can draw and redraw the line that designates any aspect of our edge. We can be high and low, proud and humble, happy and sad. We can accept the fact that we are sometimes right and sometimes wrong. We can willingly meet any challenge as best we can. We are able to change and free to try again. This is the ability to meet your edge.

CHAPTER NINE
Alignment Perception Strategies

Once we step onto our sticky mat, the tendency toward cognition should be put aside. Our perception of yoga asana might be influenced by our intellectual and analytical studies. But the experience is primarily determined by the alignment perception strategy that we consciously or unconsciously choose to employ.

There are two possible alignment perception strategies available to us during any type of sensori-motor learning. They are called the 'seeing alignment' strategy and the 'sensing alignment' strategy. 'Seeing alignment' is a natural human ability using sight. In this strategy, our minds take an image and direct our bodies to recreate that image based on memory and visual impressions. The mind relies on image recognition to make a comparison based on outward appearance.

In the 'seeing' strategy, the student observes, memorizes, and imitates the movements or positions that she sees the instructor perform. The strength of this strategy is that visual input allows for a quick motor response, but its weakness is that it overlooks the details and nuances of the experience. 'Seeing alignment' is most successful and necessary during movement-based activities and for skills requiring conformity. It is the strategy of choice for the Participant-consciousness who revels in moments of 'doing.'

For the 'seeing alignment' strategy, competency is determined by comparison (matching a specific image) or judgment (attaining a predetermined standard). The primary motive of individuals who rely exclusively on the 'seeing alignment' strategy is a constant need for self-improvement due to feelings of vulnerability, separation, and the compulsive urge for competition.

If the 'seeing' strategy provides answers to the question of "What," then the 'sensing' strategy provides answers to the questions "How" and "Why." 'Sensing alignment' encourages the student to tune into her internal environment so that she can consciously feel or sense the the proper and appropriate physical use that supports placement.

'Sensing alignment' is a slower process that requires adequate time for reflection, introspection, and conscious connection with inner sensation. Kinesthesia provides the crucial reference in this strategy. We rely on our kinesthetic awareness to monitor the body's internal environment. We also use it to observe the body's relationship to the external environment and to gravity. 'Sensing alignment' is the strategy of choice for the Observer-consciousness. It is also the primary strategy during moments of 'being.'

For the 'sensing alignment' strategy, competency is considered an individualized phenomenon that is determined by the degree of comfort and satisfaction within the self. 'Sensing alignment' is a non–conformity strategy that honors any and all perceptual experiences, no matter how ordinary or outrageous. The primary motive of individuals who rely on the 'sensing' strategy is self-sufficiency. For the most part, students who prefer this strategy have an internal locus of control. They have no attachment to the concept of perfection.

To summarize, the 'seeing alignment' strategy is outer-referential. The student is watching and trying to imitate the instructor. The 'sensing alignment' strategy is inner-referential. The student is tuning into her own body to feel the inner sensations of her personal somatic use. The 'sensing alignment' strategy supports the transformative process of yoga asana. It makes us slow down and direct our focus inward so that we bring our full awareness to the subtleties of a movement or a posture.

Comparison Chart of the Alignment Perception Strategies

Strategy:	seeing	sensing
Key sense:	sight	kinesthesia
Source of input:	external form (shape, image)	internal feeling (sensation)
Quality of input:	overt (blatant, gross)	subtle (mild, minute)
Specific cues:	comparison-based	relationship-based
Evaluation basis:	It looks right. right = accurate	It feels right. right = effortless
Purpose:	to recreate the image	to reduce tension and attain ease

Active and Passive

We can also approach yoga asana from different directions regarding qualities associated with the nature of the practice. These two perspectives are called the active and passive voices, but they could also be referred to as active and introspective. The difference between the active and the passive is found in the intent, process, attitude, and specific techniques of execution in asana.

The active mode indicates orientation toward action and creation. Passive indicates introspection and the tendency toward a steady state of complacency. It is important to recognize that passive does not imply submission or lack of intention. The passive participant is not removing himself from the experience. He is still meeting and interacting. This introspective voice merely suggests a lessening in degree of participation and an overall shift in intention. It might be useful to think of passive as a greatly reduced degree of active.

Each voice is important because it provides a valid approach to the asana experience and to the life experience. Neither is better or worse. They are just different. They are complementary, like the flip sides of a coin.

Through a balanced program that is thoughtfully designed, an accomplished Yoga instructor should be able to offer her students the challenge and inspiration of experiencing both voices. The following chart shows the general tendencies of the active and passive voices in asana.

Modality	Active / Action	Passive / Introspection
Approach	views asana as goal	views asana as process
Focus	improvement progress accomplishment steady, stable specific strong	in the moment open-minded non-habitual flowing, flexibility general submissive
Personality	Type A: Striver One who strives	Type B: Seeker One who seeks

Modality	Active / Action	Passive / Introspection
Learning style	1st – visual/auditory 2nd – somatic	1st – somatic 2nd – visual/auditory
Mental role	mind-sharpening	mind-stilling
Physical role	"doing" the pose	"being" the pose
Role of self	Participant (involved)	Observer (detached)
Relationship	separate self; "I am" as an individual	universal self; "I am" as the whole
Locus of control	external - Dependant; needs authority figure to validate the self	internal - Independent; able to affirm own choices and worth
Assessment	how the pose looks	how the pose feels
Pace	prefers faster pace	prefers slower pace
Duration	poses held briefly	poses held longer
Feedback	visual cues and instructor comments	feelings, sensations
Verbal cues	push, pull, force, press, tighten, firm, tense, compress	allow, soften, float, free, release, open loosen, yield
Energy	expended	released/conserved
Effort	medium to high	moderate, low, or none at all

Many paths, many perspectives

We have many possible paths to explore when practicing yoga asana. We can choose to work from the inside – out, or from the outside – in. We can visualize images of the body or we can work purely by inner sensation. We can analyze and intellectualize the experience or we can detach and learn by intuition.

All of these tracks are valid. Some appeal to us instantly, while others seem beyond our current level of interest or understanding. Each perspective sheds light on the same target, but they approach the subject from a slightly different angle.

The final concept that contributes to the creation of the Observer-consciousness is the breath. Direct, personal experience of the respiratory process is necessary to understand the significance of the breath. The breath plays a key role as an intermediary device between the body and the mind. The breath is the most accurate, immediate, and profound indicator of the state of the body and the mind. It is a valuable somatic resource that normally lies beyond our conscious awareness.

Enlighten Your Body

CHAPTER TEN

The Breath

It was 5:15 A.M. I was sitting on a folded blanket in my early morning meditation. As usual, I was embarking on another normal day and another standard meditation. Nothing was out of the ordinary. Nothing was different. I wasn't doing anything that I hadn't done a thousand times before. I was just going about the daily practice. Then all of sudden something really extraordinary happened! This remarkable occurrence was something I never would have anticipated!

What happened was this - I took a breath *and so did everyone else!* At that exact moment every living being on this planet that breathes took a breath along with me. I was absolutely aware that we were all breathing together. I was aware that we were all alive together. I understood that we were all ONE.

This revelation was more than a thought or idea. It was a visceral experience. I felt the oneness. I knew the oneness. I understood the oneness. I was grateful to our Earth and the Universe for providing what we, the creatures of the Earth, need to stay alive. For that one moment, everything about the interrelationships of life on Earth made perfect sense to me. We are all connected by the breath.

The Mind-Body Intersection

My breathing revelation of oneness was very significant. I learned that the breath is an essential connection device. It is a common bond shared by all creatures that must breathe to survive. But the breath also serves as a connection device within each individual. It acts as a communication channel that bridges the body and the mind.

This crucial connection, which is sometimes referred to as the 'mind-body intersection,' suggests two important ideas. First, it suggests that a direct relationship or an ongoing state of communication exists between the body and the mind. Second, it suggests that the breath supports continuity between the body and the mind. As the intermediary, the breath is influenced by the state of the body as well as the state of the mind. Even the breathing process itself has a direct effect on the mind-body connection. Regulation of the breath can alter both the mind and the body. It can potentially change the responses of both.

A steady breath coincides with a steady mind and a relaxed body, while a lack of proper respiration indicates an anxious mind and a tense body.

For the most part, breathing is an unconscious, seemingly automatic somatic activity. It does not require conscious attention or direction. As we go about our lives, we are not cognizant of the fact that we are breathing. Though breathing seems to happen more or less automatically, responsibility for regulation of the respiratory process lies in the associated musculature. As a result, breathing is directly affected by our physical health and bodily use.

Good breathing is a pre-requisite for and a feature of proper posture. Unfortunately, postural problems that distort or limit proper breathing capabilities are common. Such problems include rounded or hunched shoulders, a collapsed, narrowed chest, and a shortened spacing between the ribcage and pelvis. Two of the most prevalent postural problems are a protruding abdomen which lacks good tone and forward head syndrome. Associated breathing irregularities include shallow, frequent breathing or heavy, labored breathing, a shortened exhale, and the reverse-breathing pattern.

Many yoga poses, particularly restorative poses, are designed to stretch the musculature of the breathing mechanism. These include chest-opening poses, poses that lengthen and stretch the spinal column, poses that release tight shoulders, and simple twists to restore spinal flexibility. This easy variation of the fish pose (pictured below) helps to counteract many of the postural problems that affect the quality of our respiration.

easy fish pose

Characteristics of Proper Breathing

A solid understanding of respiration and the use of imagery can help us visualize the body's breathing process. For example, most people do not realize that a full, natural breath requires the abdomen, ribcage, chest, and back to be free from tension. Ideally, all of these bodily parts facilitate the respiratory process.

During inspiration, the thorax of the body should expand in three directions – anterior-posterior, superior-inferior, and lateral. The anterior-posterior expansion involves a forward swelling of the abdomen coupled with equal expansion of the lower and middle back. The superior-inferior expansion extends the thoracic vertebrae to their natural limit. The lateral expansion is felt as a broadening or widening in the ribcage, particularly in the area of the floating ribs. Also look for a widening between the shoulder blades and lateral movement just below the armpits.

One last anatomical adjustment that supports successful respiration occurs in the throat. Upon inspiration, the throat should open as wide as possible. The visualization of sucking the breath in through a big straw helps create the feeling of an unobstructed channel. In general, the more relaxed the body, the better the breathing. When the body's musculature is free from unnecessary tension, it will accommodate the natural movement of the breath.

❖ Inquiry # 16:   "Movements of the breath"

Concept: In this inquiry, we use imagery to achieve the sensation of an open breathing tube. We will also experience the three part movement of natural respiration in our bodies. This movement consists of sequential bodily expansions that occur upon inhalation. In order of occurrence they are (1) anterior / posterior movement in the abdominal region (lowest chamber), (2) lateral movement in the ribcage region (middle chamber), and (3) superior / inferior movement in the core (upper region).

❖ Inquiry #16a: "Sucking on a straw"

Concept: In this inquiry, we use the image of sucking on a straw to facilitate breathing.

Directions: Imagine that a straw extends through your nostrils and all the way down your throat. Upon inhalation and exhalation, visualize the breath being 'sucked' into and 'blown' out of your lungs via the passageway provided by the straw. This image helps to reduce constriction in the throat by promoting the image of a wide open channel.

❖ Inquiry # 16b: "Abdominal balloon"

Concept: In this inquiry, we use imagery to facilitate lower chamber breathing.

Discussion: Just about every yoga class has at least one person who is horrified to discover that they are a reverse-breather. Reverse-breathing means that the abdomen drops inward toward the spine upon inhalation and swells outward upon exhalation. The easiest and most rational explanation of the proper breathing pattern is to picture a balloon inside one's tummy. When the air flows into the body to fill the lungs, the balloon in the abdomen expands as it inflates. When the air flows out of the body to empty the lungs, the balloon deflates.

Inquiry # 16b: "Abdominal balloon"

Imagery such as this is an effective and handy way of teaching breathing, placement, use, and other concepts. Imagery and visualization bypass the logical, cognitive thinking processes that require conscious attention. Imagery and visualization work very efficiently by activating the subconscious mind which allows us to tap into our innate conceptual awareness.

Directions: Imagine that a deflated balloon is located inside your abdomen. It is lodged in a position one or two inches above the navel and exactly halfway between the front and back sides of your body.

Place the tips of your middle fingers at the navel and let the hands rest on the abdomen. In this inquiry, the hands act as the Observer-consciousness. The abdominal movement that occurs in conjunction with the diaphragm's activation represents the Participant.

Upon inhalation, the balloon inflates to produce a gentle swelling of the abdomen. Upon exhalation, the balloon deflates and the tummy flattens inward toward the spine.

❖ Inquiry # 16c: "Wing expansion"

Concept: In this inquiry, we use the image of a bird's wing expansion to facilitate middle chamber breathing.

Directions: Place your hands alongside the lateral edge of the ribs, so that your arms are positioned somewhat like a bird's wings.

Inquiry # 16c: "Wing expansion"

Gently press inward with the hands while exhaling completely to empty the lungs. Let the forthcoming inspiration be slow, deep, and full, so that the ribcage obviously lifts and swells laterally. The position of the arms and hands will also lift and widen slightly in response to the ribcage movement. Upon exhalation, the ribcage descends and narrows as it returns to its original position. The bodily movement of the breath is observed in the hands.

❖ Inquiry # 16d: "Scapular abduction"

Concept: In this inquiry, we widen the area between the scapula to facilitate upper chamber breathing.

Directions: Extend your right arm in front of you with the palm facing away from your body. Extend the left arm in front of you, with the left palm pressing against the back of the right hand. As you inhale, visualize the breath filling the space between the scapula so that this area seems to expand and widen. At the same time, press the left hand against the right, pushing both hands forward to assist in stretching the upper back.

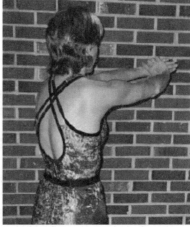

Inquiry # 16d:
"Scapular abduction"

Repetitive cues for breath work include the following:

➢ To change the breath, you need to notice the breath.
➢ Check in with your breathing.
➢ Catch yourself breathing throughout the day.
➢ Count silently to yourself as you breathe. Inhale 1-2-3-4, Exhale 1-2-3-4-."
➢ Every time you exhale, consciously release unnecessary tension from the body.
➢ Every time you exhale, silently repeat a word like relax, release, detach, or let go.
➢ Remember to relax the jaw, to soften the gaze, and to consciously release unnecessary tension as you breathe so that the movements or positions become effortless.

Breathing and the Stress Response

The internal environment of the body consists of somatic, psychological, and emotional consciousness. To meet the demand presented by a given stressor, these internal states must go on alert. They gear up so that they are prepared to deal with the challenge. This remarkable ability of the autonomic nervous system is commonly referred to as the general adaptation syndrome.

Unfortunately, the general adaptation syndrome does not differentiate between a positive and a negative event. The more or less automatic nature of the physiological changes responds equally to both types of stressors. Even if we are not consciously aware that our bodies are making adaptations, the breath registers the change.

A disturbance in the state of the breath can be caused by emotional outburst, physical trauma, or mental anguish. Because the emotions, thoughts, and unforeseen or accidental physical occurrences tend to occur so quickly ("in a split second") or so subtly ("it sneaks up on us"), we are often not consciously aware of our reaction. Our somatic reactions are reflexive, instinctive, and often beyond our conscious control.

To better understand this mind-body-breath phenomenon, let's examine the physical effects of fear. Our bodies react to fear with an acute bodily stress response. This response is called the startle reflex. It is the jumpstart mechanism of the general adaptation syndrome. The startle reflex is characterized by an elevated tension level, compression at the body's core, and inhibited breathing.

Tightness on any level of the abdominal musculature in the body's core will hinder the capacity for the full breath. If the abdominals are habitually contracted, the vital capacity is diminished. The lungs are not able to descend fully upon inspiration. Deep, internal abdominal compression causes the body to shift its breathing technique. The body resorts to breathing from an anatomically higher location – the chest.

The most common breathing malady is chest breathing. Chest breathing is very shallow breathing, which indicates a reduced vital capacity. When a person breaths exclusively in the chest, he never allows the diaphragm to fully descend upon inhalation. As a result, the lower chambers of the lungs never fill with oxygen.

Many people become chest breathers in response to a stressful lifestyle. The chest breather doesn't notice that his body is perpetually primed for fight or flight. Yet a fist fight or the need for running away seldom materializes. In today's world, fear is usually the result of feeling inadequate or unaccepted. There is no pressing calamity or crisis, and no physical danger is actually present. But as long as the mind perceives any possibility of a threat, the body prepares itself for fight or flight.

If the body does not have the opportunity to discharge or release its somatic stress adaptations, some of the symptoms will hang on. As the somatic emergency response occurs more frequently, the body begins to function in a state of alert. The body is habitually tense, the breathing is habitually restricted, and the mind remains on the defensive. For the soma, new learning has occurred. Physical characteristics of the stress response are now accepted and recognized as the body's natural state.

Because the stress response and chest breathing are so prevalent in our society, yoga instructors spend a lot of time promoting the necessity of bringing the breath into the lower lungs. This practice is referred to as abdominal breathing or diaphragmatic breathing. The full and natural qualities of abdominal breathing are only possible in a body that is relaxed and comfortable.

Stretch, Relax, and Breathe

The ability to stretch and the ability to relax enhance breath work. For example, in the standing forward fold pose the front side of the body becomes more and more compressed as hip flexion ability increases. Because the body's front side is deeply compressed, the breath must move into the body's backside. If the musculature of the upper back is not free enough to allow expansion of the incoming breath, breathing will be restricted - even thought the basic image of the pose itself looks good.

standing forward fold

96

The same circumstances exist during the seated forward fold pose. In this case, the breath must be able to flow unimpeded into the lower back. Both poses demonstrate how optimal respiration requires the necessity of natural flexibility in the complete musculature.

seated forward fold

Tension stifles the body's ability to take a full breath. When the body is tense, the diaphragm is held tight and cannot fully descend. If the diaphragm does not descend, the lungs never inflate to their full capacity and the body does not function at its best. This is why general relaxation techniques that will alleviate unnecessary bodily tension and release the diaphragm are an important component in restoring the body's capacity for proper respiration. A relaxed body that allows natural movement of the diaphragm is essential to a state of well-being.

The relaxed and non-competitive nature of asana absolutely supports better breathing! The state of physical stillness and tranquility produced by asana is complementary to steady, full, and healthy respiration. Likewise, the restoration of the natural breathing process enhances the essential experience of asana. For this reason, it is important to rehearse the experience of breathing in separate body parts to assure that we feel the movement throughout. Specifically, we should be able to differentiate the respiratory sensations as follows:

> ➢ The abdomen swells forward upon inhalation, and the navel drops back inward toward the spine upon exhalation.

> ➢ The upper posterior ribs (under the armpits) widen or expand laterally upon inhalation. Then the ribcage deflates, contracting toward the core upon exhalation.

- ➤ The lower back (near the kidneys / just below the lowest rib) widens and swells upon inhalation.

- ➤ The area between the shoulder blades widens, and the superior posterior aspect of the shoulders lifts slightly upon inhalation.

- ➤ The incoming breath may be felt as fullness in the throat and sinuses. To allow this movement, the jaw must be relaxed and the tongue must rest heavily at its base.

- ➤ We can visualize three bodily diaphragms to help us experience the feeling of respiratory fullness. (1) The vocal diaphragm is located at the top of the throat. (2) The respiratory diaphragm is located at the level of the lower ribs. (3) The abdominal diaphragm is located at the level of the perineum. Upon inhalation, visualize the vocal diaphragm swelling upward to contain the top of the breath. The respiratory and abdominal diaphragms swell downward to contain the bottom of the breath.

Relaxation techniques are important for restoring health. They complement the stretching work provided by yoga asana. Relaxation helps us reset the normal resting tone of our muscles by lowering their habitual tension level. We practice relaxation techniques to reduce the body's tension, just as we might take blood pressure pills to reduce our blood pressure. If the body is not relaxed, the potential energy available to the body is curtailed. Basic breath work, physical techniques such as yoga asana, and relaxation techniques should be recommended as part of a complete program designed to promote health and fitness.

Breathing Traps

Breathing is a natural and subtle process. Refining the quality of the breath is not something that can be hurried. Sometimes an overzealous approach to re-establishing good breathing habits actually produces additional breathing problems. The two most common breathing 'traps' include (1) an overemphasis of the inferior (abdominal) aspect of breathing, and (2) an overemphasis of the anterior (front side of the body) aspect of breathing.

In the first case, the focus on drawing the breath downward into the lower chambers of the lungs becomes overemphasized. We get so caught up in the abdominal aspect of breathing that we forget about the chest or upper body breathing. Yet the upper chambers provide the crucial link to the head and the brain. Relaxed musculature in the neck and jaw will facilitate upper chamber breathing.

In the second case, we tend to forget that the breath should also move into the body's posterior side. Symbolically, the back represents our support system. Our awareness or lack of awareness of the movement of the breath in our backs signifies how well we can rally our support system. We certainly don't want to 'turn our backs' on our own support system!

Unfortunately, the natural breathing experience is by no means common or ordinary. But it is an extremely powerful sensation that profoundly changes our perspective. The sensation of free flowing diaphragmatic movement symbolizes a somatic connection with our life force. When we live and breathe in a body that is free of physical restrictions and mental inhibitions, we *know* that we are not the one doing the breathing. We are the one being breathed! This is a direct, personal experience of the energetic force that inhabits and sustains the life of the body.

PART THREE
Clarifying the Psyche

We make improvements in our bodies by rehearsing new patterns of use and creating better postural alignment. These physical improvements are acquired through enhanced awareness and somatic insights. As we gradually change and improve the body, we are often surprised to find that we have begun to change in other ways, as well. What effect do these physical changes have on the psyche?

Perhaps you no longer react reflexively in an emotionally charged situation. Perhaps you have begun to consider another person's viewpoint during an argument or discussion. Maybe you have even backed down or apologized for a misunderstanding. Maybe you no longer beat yourself up for not getting an A on the final exam. Perhaps heavy traffic doesn't provoke you the way it used too. These are all examples of how positive somatic changes gradually and subtly begin to affect the psyche. If the state of the body and the state of the mind are reflections of one another, then a relaxed and comfortable body must coincide with a mind that is steady and calm. Physical equilibrium mirrors mental equanimity.

Just as we sought to identify poor somatic habits in an effort to make positive changes in the body, we now seek their cognitive counterpart. To identify negative cognitive tendencies, we must thoroughly examine our habitual ways of thinking. But observing and analyzing the psyche is easier said than done. The simplest, most direct way to begin this process is to *pay close attention to the body*. We can observe our bodies to find out if we are unknowingly harboring negative mental activity. Somatic symptoms indicate the presence of problematic psychological constructs, i.e. unresolved 'regrets.'

Conscious bodily awareness is undermined by the mind's desire to scatter, flee, over-analyze, or succumb to emotional outburst. If the mind wanders, the body will blindly resort to its old habits. Keeping the mind focused on the task at hand is a challenging requirement that we cannot disregard. This is why a large part of the transformation process involves observing and managing the psyche. Transformation is not finalized until we clarify the psyche.

Clarifying the psyche means addressing the underlying psychological cause of inappropriate or undesirable responses. We clarify the psyche by identifying and questioning our issues and illusions. Unfortunately, negative mental constructs normally reside at a subliminal level. Below the threshold of conscious perception, these psychological obstacles are difficult to access.

Psychological obstacles include *addictions* – such as the addiction to fear and the addiction to comfort, *assumptions* – such as 'an attractive person is a nice person,' and *beliefs* – such as 'hard work pays off.' They also include any other orientation or inclination that advocates limitation-thinking.

The Observer-consciousness is responsible for locating and examining inappropriate psychological obstacles. Then the Participant-consciousness is responsible for activating specific changes that will correct them.

CHAPTER ELEVEN
Change

When I was twenty-two and a half, I went to my first yoga class. I remember that I was twenty-two *and a half* because it was such a critical moment in my life. After the final relaxation, I sat up and knew I had been changed. Profoundly changed. A Christian might say that I had been born again. A mystic might say that I had been saved. At the time, I wasn't sure exactly what had happened. But I knew it was meaningful and valuable.

I walked home floating a foot off the ground. Life was good and I was special. In one way, I felt more alive than I had ever felt before. The world and its people were especially vibrant. Everything was more real and more immediate than I remembered. In another way, I felt like I was dreaming with my eyes wide open.

It was as if the whole world were contained inside a magnificent crystal ball, while I stood on the outside looking in. Somehow I had emerged from this heavenly sphere and was no longer an indoctrinated inhabitant. I was no longer permanently bound by its logic, structure, and rules. I was filled to the brim with a newfound sense of freedom and possibilities. From that moment on, my life turned around. I totally changed the direction I was going.

Possibilities

During asana's honeymoon period, the neophyte yoga practitioner has reveled in moments of newfound possibilities. He has tasted relaxation, acceptance, harmony, inspiration, and personal empowerment. He feels more in touch with his body. He has even learned a lot about himself. In small ways, his relationships have improved. He is often happier and more content. But eventually the same old patterns emerge. He gets tired, irritable, unstable, and unsure. Things start going wrong or life gets hard again. He can't help but wonder why.

By this time, the yoga student has made the connection between somatic sensations that have been awakened through yoga asana and improvements in his self. He has begun to examine the unconscious nature of his habitual choices. He notices that certain behaviors, acquaintances, activities, and foods no longer agree with him. He questions his own intent, commitment, and purpose. He might even contemplate whether he should continue with the particular course of his life or change directions.

Perhaps he has the distinct impression that happiness, health, and personal transformation could become a permanent fixture in his daily life. But one tremendous hurdle still remains before the real work of transformation begins. Is he willing and able to make the necessary changes?

It doesn't take long for yoga practitioners to discover that the asana experience is somehow changing them, improving them. But steady progress on the path of self improvement will be hindered if they do not learn to successfully deal with change. If our lifetime occupation involves evolution of the self, the ability to deal with change is an essential skill.

For most of us, change is a problem because we don't like it. We don't like change because it provokes us. It demands our attention and it requires a response. Change represents something new or unfamiliar that we must figure out how to deal with. It's like a puzzle that needs to be solved. It can be an aggravation, a dilemma, or a challenge. Though somewhat threatening and sometimes unmanageable, change can also be a positive experience that is very beneficial. Change offers an opportunity for growth.

The Comfort Zone

The Comfort Zone is a particular area, time period, or state of being in which an individual experiences a sense of well-being, relief, consolation, refreshment, and rest. When we are operating within our CZ, we are at ease. We are familiar with our established ways of thinking, behaving, and being. We do not feel threatened. Time spent in the CZ lets us assimilate recently acquired knowledge and experiences. During this time, the individual prepares himself to experience future growth.

Our CZ also includes certain mental parameters. These parameters cause us to define, judge, and direct our own behaviors as well as those of others. Problems arise when people construct their CZ for negative, self-limiting reasons that are based on needs and fears. For example, the control freak fears chaos. The approval-seeker fears rejection, while the overscheduled person fears loneliness. People operating from any of these needs or fears will prefer the safety and familiarity of their CZ.

Yet the average CZ has relatively narrow boundaries. We can't go very far. We can't do very much. In many ways, living within our CZ is like never leaving our own backyard. Even though we know there is a big world beyond our fence posts, we never get to experience it.

Usually, the impetus for growth occurs when the individual arrives at a crossroads or a decision-making time in his life. If a person wants to grow or to learn, he must choose to temporarily suspend the security of the CZ. (This is the rationale behind the concept of the *edge* in asana). The decision to leave the CZ could be based on a steadily advancing sense of discomfort with one's present state. Or it might be prompted by a shocking and significant life event. Either way, change is imminent.

Asana as a Vehicle for Growth

Yoga asana is a psycho-somatic challenge that is designed to bring about change. The first thing asana does is show us our habituation toward comfort. It points out our preference for remaining within the safety of our Comfort Zone. Though we think we thrive in the face of comfort and familiarity, in reality the status quo breeds stagnation. We must be willing to venture outside of the CZ if we are to have experiences which will promote our potential.

Asana is a somatic method that encourages us to think outside the box of our current CZ. Though a certain amount of familiarity, consistency, and continuity are needed in the asana experience, we must not fall victim to expectations and predefined standards. Comfort and familiarity can easily become addictive. But they can also stifle our curiosity for exploration and growth.

Asana is most effective when it provides continuity but still allows freedom for opportunity. To allow freedom in the body's response during asana practice, we need to recall only the most elementary cues for placement in the pose. For example, if the body spoke in sentences, it would say something like this: "In the seated forward fold pose, I sit upright on the floor with legs stretched out in front. I fold the front side of my torso over my legs and then I relax."

Basic cues with minimal instruction keep the experience fresh. Your body is smart. If you let it, it will instinctively accommodate the pose to the best of its ability. Interestingly enough, the hardest part of asana is not the physical part. The hardest and most important part of asana is learning to remain psychologically neutral.

seated forward fold pose

Psychologically neutral means that we are not expecting anything to happen in the pose. We are not anticipating a certain experience. We are not hoping that it will be a good practice. We are not worrying that it will be a bad practice. We are not trying to avoid the sensation of pain, nor are we hoping to be swept away in a moment of bliss. We do not want to recreate a picture of a pose that we saw in a book or on a video. We do not need to match yesterday's degree of accomplishment. As much as possible, we do not rely on previous experiences to define or confine the present moment. *We have brought no agenda to the pose.*

Because we have no agenda, we are able to be purely present as the experience unfolds moment by moment. We are totally immersed in the now. In a supportive yet detached state of neutrality, we are open to the possibility of leaving our CZ. We are willing to adapt because we are receptive and responsive. We are also responsible. This means that we are ready, willing, and able to deal with the status of the body and mind as they are right now.

Our only goal is to deal with today's challenge today. We are not interested in yesterday's challenge or tomorrow's challenge. Our personal journey is marked by this particular meeting of the body and the mind. An inquiry into the meaning of the present moment is all we ask – no more and no less.

On a purely physical level, many asanas directly challenge the physical nature of our CZ. Asanas give us the opportunity to put our bodies in a different relationship with gravity. This is a difficult lesson, for many of these body positions are uncomfortable and highly unfamiliar.

Topsy-turvy, twisted, or other unconventional poses put our bodies in a new and unfamiliar position. These poses deny us the basic human stance of an upright, vertical carriage on two feet. They challenge us to see how we will respond physically, emotionally, and mentally. Situations that alter our habitual relationship to gravity require uncharacteristic usage of musculature, circulation, breathing, and thinking. In yoga, these unfamiliar situations include single leg standing balances, inverted, seated, supine, and prone postures.

Single leg standing balances change the body's base of support. Most of us don't spend a lot of time standing on one foot. We are not used to the adaptations required to maintain vertical balance. Many students practicing single leg standing balances look like the rug has been pulled out from under their feet. They wobble and waver and sometimes even hop around, as if this were the most impossible task!

Inverted asanas turn the world as we know it upside down. During inversions, many of us experience a sense of utter displacement. We may feel unique circulatory sensations. We may experience peculiar feelings of pressure and fullness in the pelvis or chest. The lower extremities may tingle or shake, while the upper extremities may feel too weak to support the position. Our respiration might feel a bit strained or suffocated. We will probably need to modify our breathing patterns while inverted. Overall, inversions provoke very foreign somatic sensations, so we must approach these poses carefully. Initially, we should refrain from holding inversions too long.

You'd think that everyone would feel comfortable performing standing poses. But I find that students either like standing poses a lot or they don't like them at all. Some students would be happy to do a whole class of standing work. Others can't wait to get down on the floor. Students who don't like standing poses feel like all of their inadequacies are on display, while students who like standing poses enjoy feeling powerful and dominant. An egocentric student will prefer standing poses over floor work. This type of student doesn't like it when seated poses 'level the playing field.'

Seated poses, supine, or prone poses literally 'knock us off our feet.' Again, a big part of the yoga challenge is the unfamiliar base of support. But plenty of students actually prefer these poses. I am one of them. Some of us like these poses because they are seem safe and stable. You can't fall down from a seated pose. At least, you can't fall too far. To a certain extent, removing the fear of falling also removes the fear of *failure.*

Seated poses challenge us to approach life from a lower position that represents a more humble perspective. Poses where we have already been 'knocked off of our feet' teach us to diminish judgment and let go of frustration. We feel less visible and less exposed as we come nearer to the ground.

In truth, the greatest obstacle in floor work is habitual tension. The challenge is to relax and surrender to gravity. Supine or prone poses performed on a hard surface are a wonderful way to induce realignment. In all poses, but especially during floor work, gravity is one of our best teachers. It is the body's basic vehicle for restoration.

A big part of the asana lesson is being ready, willing, and able to embrace the ongoing changes in our somas and in our psyches. Each time we practice a particular asana, the basic shape of our body in the pose is always the same. At the same time, something is always different in the pose. Something is always fresh, new, and unique. These are the details that we are looking for. We can use these immediate insights to push back the boundaries of our CZ.

CHAPTER 12

Assumptions

I worried every time I read a report about a guru who had fallen from grace. I couldn't understand how a spiritual teacher could do bad things. How could they act like that? Perhaps it was because they weren't as pure-hearted as they seemed to be. Perhaps they had been deceiving their followers all along. If spiritual leaders could go astray, I wondered if there was any hope for the rest of us.

Should we of the common herd just give up trying to be good people? Should we just forget about the dream of achieving enlightenment? Should we accept the fact that no one in the whole world is absolutely pure, true, and trustworthy? I, for one, didn't like thinking that we were fated to be a simple-minded society of blundering, warmongering humans.

The fact that spiritual people could do bad things or think impure thoughts continued to haunt me. I decided to keep a close eye on any spiritual leader that crossed my path. I grew suspicious of any individual that acted holier-than-thou. I kept my distance and observed their behaviors carefully. Were they too good to be true? I wanted undeniable proof that they were really walking their talk.

Somehow this predicament reminded me of my old 'regrets' dilemma. In much the same way, I agonized and analyzed the situation for quite some time but couldn't reach an acceptable conclusion. Finally I just gave up. I didn't want to keep worrying about it. I told myself that I no longer cared if there was a correlation between ethical behavior and spirituality or not. Secretly, I assumed I'd stumble across the truth eventually.

Ten or eleven years passed. Then out of the blue, I found what I had been looking for! I was casually flipping through a magazine while sitting in a doctor's waiting room. You can imagine my surprise when I came upon an article about spiritual improprieties. Eagerly, I began to read. I couldn't help hoping that this article contained the answer to my question.

In a nutshell, this is what the article said: First, it confirmed that we all *assume* advanced spirituality corresponds to a clear, pure mind. We think that a spiritual person is a good person. But this article also stated that (just as I had discovered) 'it ain't necessarily so.' This is because the spiritual and the psychological are two separate aspects of the self.

You can be spiritually adept without being psychologically clear. This means that someone who partakes of daily rituals can appear to be extremely evolved. But if he hasn't directly addressed the maladies of the psyche, his spirituality lacks depth and absolute sincerity.

Likewise, a body that looks pretty good on the outside can conceal inner compression, misalignment, or lack of nourishment. The seeds of physical illness and remnants of psychological cobwebs run deep. They can remain hidden for a long, long time. But indications of these problems will eventually find their way to the surface.

Nowadays, a lot of us include spiritual practices in our daily regime. I believe that we do this because we truly want to be good people. We memorize prayers, perform rituals, and put on the holiest of demeanors. Though we might dress in white from head to toe and speak softly, many of us carry a big stick hidden behind our backs. Outwardly, our appearance and actions scream 'spirituality.' But on the inside we're armed and ready to take a whack at anyone who bothers us or gets in our way!

Here's an example of an everyday individual – a person who is not so different from you or me – that was stuck in this psycho-spiritual dilemma: This fabulous lady happened to be a yoga instructor. She was cheerful, talkative, and physically fit. Everyone liked her. Her smile was warm and wide. She was very pretty. In every conversation, she mentioned how peaceful, blissful, and spiritual she was. On the surface, she appeared to be all of these wonderful things.

But if you took a closer look, you would see that her jaw was rigid. When she spoke, her lips articulated the words but the jaw didn't move at all. Sometimes she made a funny or cute comment that was tinged with nasty sarcasm. These revealing details suggested that this friendly lady was not exactly what she appeared to be.

Don't get me wrong. I said this lady was fabulous and I meant it. I liked her a lot. She was definitely spiritual. She was a wonderful yoga teacher. She was a really nice person that was a lot of fun to be with. But the telltale details of her behavior indicated that she hadn't done her psychological homework. In spite of her spiritual expertise and those frequent proclamations of virtue, she had never thoroughly examined her psyche. Like cobwebs from the past, she harbored some negative habits. This lady needed to get busy cleaning up her own 'dirt.' She needed to clear her psyche.

Surprisingly enough, the rigidity of her jaw and those tart comments were minute details that most people would simply overlook. People tend to see what they *think* they see or what they *want* to see, instead of what's really there. If we want to like someone, we will like them. We'll classify them as a nice person or a good person. We'll notice all the wonderful details about them that support our decision to like them. We'll be quick to overlook their bad stuff because we don't want to acknowledge it. The tendency to classify and label other people is something that we are all guilty of. When we do this, we are operating via our underlying assumptions.

In a similar fashion, many people evaluate expertise in yoga based on how well someone can perform an asana. The error in thinking is due to assumptions based on purely physical attributes. The naturally flexible person or the person with a background in gymnastics is often mistaken for an accomplished yogi. We assume that this person has mastered asana because he can make the pose look effortless. In reality he is performing a stunt. What he has mastered is only the veneer of the asana experience.

For the inflexible student or the student with an anatomical anomaly, accomplishment in the pose does not come easily. This type of student recognizes the fact that asana is a demanding process of re-education. He intuitively understands that mastery of asana is the result of cognitive and somatic understandings that are thorough and significant. For this student, improvements are not quick, obvious, or exclamatory. His accomplishment is a purely personal matter, and he is unaffected by what others think.

The point is that we cannot count on general appearance or everyday dialogue to provide an accurate indication of a person's inner state of being. Looks and linguistics can be deceiving. To tap into the deeper levels of consciousness, we must become aware of the revealing details that we have previously overlooked – both in others and in ourselves. To enter the realm of the subconscious, we need to sharpen our sensory awareness by improving our observational skills.

Debauched Kinesthesia

The attractive lady with the locked jaw was disconnected from her own somatic input. In her mind, she saw herself as the humble, spiritual person that she wanted to be. For the most part, her behaviors validated this belief. But the deeper details of her self showed that she still had psychological lessons to learn.

Just like this pretty lady, there are many people who are accustomed to functioning with subconscious tension, denial, or dissatisfaction. These folks are not trying to be deceptive. They honestly don't realize the lack of harmony between their body and their mind. They mistakenly accept problematic somatic manifestations as their natural state of being. This false belief based on inaccurate awareness is referred to as debauched kinesthesia.

When a person suffers from debauched kinesthesia, it means that he has lost the ability to differentiate between the natural state (of relaxation) and the habitual state (of tension and compensations). In essence, he doesn't recognize or cannot identify his own somatic sensations.

In debauched kinesthesia, we blindly believe that we are what we think we are. We believe what we want to see or what we want to hear. But the reality of our somatic input often registers something very different. A clear example of such blind belief in cognitive illusions is the anorexic girl who thinks she is fat. If she could accurately examine her somatic reality, it would be obvious that she is remarkably thin, and that her mind has deceived her.

Unfortunately, debauched kinesthesia has become commonplace. With our senses somewhat numbed by the hustle and bustle of daily life, we respond out of sheer habit. Sometimes we are surprised when we suddenly 'wake up' right in the middle of a bizarre, unhealthy, or emotionally-poisoned situation. We desperately wonder why this happened to us.

What we overlook is how we got there. We got there because we were completely unaware of our habitual responses, stereotypical behaviors, and imbedded relationship patterns. We got there because we weren't able to see that which is closest to us – those habitually defining elements of our own soma and psyche.

The people that we spend a lot of time with are often more familiar with our physical and psychological patterns than we ourselves are. Even in silhouette, our family and friends could probably identify us. They could probably predict our reactions in a variety of situations, based on their knowledge of our habitual behavioral patterns.

On one level, our general physical characteristics define who we are by establishing each of us as a recognizable image. But each of us also has specific behavioral, mental, and emotional characteristics that define the individuality of the self. If we want to improve or change any of our own self-defining characteristics, we must first learn how to accurately identify them.

Thus the solution to debauched kinesthesia is the advanced awareness of the Observer consciousness. The Observer perspective teaches us to rely on more than our cognition and our assumptions. This perspective recognizes that there are other forms of guidance. The Observer knows that we are not just what we do. It knows that we are also what we think about. We are our relationships. And we are our somas.

Our bodies reflect who and what we really are.

The Power of the Psyche

If I were to ask "Why do you experience pain, soreness, and suffering when you practice yoga asana?" your immediate answer would consist of physical maladies. You would talk about stiffness, old age, lack of athletic ability, arthritis, etc.

But what if I asked "Why are you so miserable, unsatisfied, or bored with your daily life?" In this case, you would pause to contemplate your reasons before you answered. It's unlikely that your answer would focus solely on physical problems. You would realize that the problem is much more complex. You would acknowledge that the problem involves the psyche.

If we take a closer look at the asana experience, we will find that what troubles us the most is not the limitations of the body. What troubles us the most is – just like in daily life - the psyche! This is why a large part of our work in yoga applies to re-educating the psyche.

The most valuable lessons that we learn from yoga asana are not techniques that teach us to stand properly, breathe properly, or execute a perfected asana. Asana teaches much more than a series of sensori-motor skills.

The details of the physical body are fairly easy to see. But what we are really learning about are the details that remain unseen. We are learning about the details of the *self.* The details of the self include our underlying cognitive tendencies. We cannot overlook the necessity of addressing the psyche if we want to truly understand the self.

Enlighten Your Body

CHAPTER THIRTEEN
Priorities

Back in the early 80's, I took an unorthodox sabbatical from college. Much to the dismay of my parents and friends, I sold everything I owned and journeyed from Chicago to Los Angeles to study yoga. When I arrived at my destination, I joined an odd and assorted group of fellow travelers. I was a seeker. Like all the others, I was searching for a new way of being.

We were all 'broken' when we arrived at the little scientific yoga studio in sunny southern California. Coming together from different lifestyles, different backgrounds, different ages, and different parts of the country, this unlikely group of comrades longed to discover a path, lifestyle, or existence that provided meaning and hope.

We practiced yoga every day and spent hours together discussing philosophy, gurus, ashrams, and such. We contemplated 'new age' techniques like acupuncture and healing with pendulums. Growing, learning, sharing, gaining strength and renewing confidence, we were all getting healed.

During this time, every one of us formed new dreams. We built or rebuilt something out of what we perceived to be nothing in our lives. We supported each other as we woke up, established priorities and worth, and literally came back to life. Yoga was our vehicle toward health and happiness. For this assorted group of non-traditional yogis, yoga was nothing less than *salvation*.

Not all individuals are broken when yoga comes knocking at the door of their consciousness. But a great many people do seek yoga to help them cope with issues of stress and to deal with the hectic pace of daily life.

In our present lifestyle, attributes that glorify aggression and competition are the norm. We are a driven society that thrives on comparison, a hurried pace, and over-stimulation. Today's fast-paced lifestyle is busy, productive, and active. In spite of this, many of us feel unfulfilled and lacking. We lack a sense of structure and fulfillment in our lives because we are unaware of our priorities. Without proper identification of our priorities, we cannot make a commitment to our priorities. This situation leaves us floundering and out of control.

Priorities can be used as guidelines or signposts that mark the path of your life's course. If you know your priorities, it's pretty easy to see where you are going. You know that you are on the right path. When you act in accordance to your priorities, your life has direction and purpose. But it takes some time, effort, contemplation, and perhaps some shuffling of our schedules to finally arrive at an arrangement of priorities that works best for us.

We know when our priorities are in line because our lives seem balanced. When everything is in sync, we are not aggravated or bored with what we are doing. We don't daydream or whine about what we would like to be doing. We are content. Most of us would be quick to agree that good health and happiness qualify as top priorities. Yet we continue to overlook the necessity of balancing a busy, ultra-productive, schedule-oriented lifestyle with equal time and attention allocated to nourishment, reflection, adequate rest, and refreshment.

Our dissatisfaction with the hectic lifestyle is due to the inconsistency between the priorities that social standards have imposed on us and the priorities that truly reflect our innate awareness. What we have been programmed to believe as being most important in our lives is not necessarily what is really most important in our lives. True priorities are based on 'who I am,' instead of 'who I think I should be' or 'who others tell me I am.'

Priorities are a personal matter that should be determined by what is important to each of us as a unique individual. A person's priorities should be based on the specific path and life purpose that was chosen by each individual self. Essentially, something is a priority in your life if it supports your life's path, purpose, and mission. Anything else is just a distraction.

❖ Inquiry # 17: "Essential cues"

Concept: In this inquiry, we use yoga to learn about the importance of priorities. This exercise provides a lesson in defining and establishing priorities in asana. It does this by focusing our attention on terminology and cueing for constructing the pose.

Directions: Read the five cues for the Triangle pose and study the five photos. Then follow these five sequential cues to build the pose in your own body.

1. "Take a wide stance, having one leg length between your feet."

"Take a wide stance' indicates a standing position. "Having one leg's length between your feet" provides a more exact reference for placement. It indicates that the two feet are far apart in a straddle stance. This cue specifies the positioning of the body in space. It is presented first because the most basic priority in the pose is the body's base of support. By clarifying the body's relationship to gravity, we feel grounded and secure.

2. "The spine lengthens and extends laterally from the pelvis."

The next priority in the pose is the relationship of the spine and pelvis. Relative to the pelvis, the spine is not in its anatomical (vertical) position. If this had been our first cue, we would know that the spine is folded sideways in relationship to the pelvis - but we would be unsure of the body's relationship to gravity.

3. "The torso is in line with the legs."

The priority is the relationship of the trunk to the legs. This cue suggests that the trunk and legs are positioned parallel to one another, or that they exist in a single plane.

4. "The crown of the head extends away from the tailbone."

The priority is the relationship of the head to tailbone. This cue gives more specific information about the position of the spine. It tells us that the top and bottom parts of the spinal column are reaching away from each other. The word "extend" describes maximum possible length between the spine's distal portions. This cue confirms the quality of spinal extension.

5. "The right arm reaches up and the left arm reaches down."

The priority is the relationship of the two arms. They are aligned vertically. The arms are less important to the vital construction of the pose, as they provide neither support nor stability. Their placement simply enhances the general attitude of bodily extension. For that reason, the cue regarding arm positioning is given last. For the triangle pose, this cue is lowest on the list of priorities.

Every one of these statements emphasizes placement of body parts based on their relationship to one another or to gravity. The specific order of these five cues helps the yoga student construct the pose using the most basic elements of placement first. Later cues contribute revisions that improve accuracy of alignment.

Let's review the reasons for the specific order of the cues.

(1) The first cue establishes the basic body position. We know that the Triangle is a standing position - as opposed to being seated, inverted, supine, or prone.

(2) The second cue establishes the relationship of the spine and pelvis, which is a key ingredient in any asana.

(3) The third cue more clearly and precisely defines the spinal placement.

(4) The fourth cue adds the *quality* of spinal extension.

(5) The fifth, or final cue, details the placement of the upper extremities (arms), which are the only major body part that had not been previously addressed.

Notice how the particular progression of the cues gradually fills in the necessary details. It this way, the cues help the student to zero in on precise alignment.

Now let's consider what would happen if you were not given specific sequential cues to help you perform the pose. What if you just looked at a picture of the pose and then tried to recreate it your own body? How would the asana experience be different? Would your somatic awareness be as complete? Can you see how attention to priorities makes the learning experience more fulfilling, insightful, and accurate?

You might look at the five cues for the Triangle pose in the example above and feel that there is not enough specific direction given. That may be true, but five cues is not a lot to work with. Remember, I am talking about five *essential* cues, not five cues that constitute run-on sentences.

Here's an example of an impractical cue: "Take a wide stance, having one leg's length between your feet and the right foot turned 90 degrees to the right and the left heel turned 45 degrees to the left while anchored on the back heel." This lengthy cue provides far too much information for a student to comprehend at once. In fact, this cue is so technically precise that it limits the student's opportunity for an individualized experience.

In my opinion, this statement counts as three cues – and we haven't even mentioned positioning of the spine!

1. "Take a wide stance, having one leg's length between your feet."
2. "Turn the right foot 90 degrees to the right and turn the left heel 45 degrees to the left."
3. "Anchor on the back heel."

For the past two years I have included the Essential Cues exercise in my teacher training courses for yoga instructors. Most teachers understand the concept of cueing priorities right away. However, I recall one exam where the instructor totally missed the boat. These are her five cues:

1. Bend to the side.
2. Push down through the feet.
3. Take the left arm down.
4. Take the right arm up.
5. Keep breathing.

On the side of the page she wrote a little note saying that many more cues would be needed to complete the pose. I wrote back and asked her to physically perform the cues that she had written. Then I asked her if she felt that these cues were adequate to produce a pose that looked anything at all like the Triangle pose. The lesson is that certain cues are more essential than other cues.

Here's another example. Suppose you are performing a single leg standing balance pose, but your supporting foot is weak and wobbly. In this case, would it really matter that your head to neck alignment is perfect? It wouldn't matter too much, because the first priority in any standing pose is the base of support. Without a solid support structure, the rest of the body cannot achieve stability or comfort.

The Essential Cues exercise helps us learn to prioritize by discovering exactly which cues are necessary and which cues or types of cues are superfluous to the asana experience. We need to be able to differentiate between cues that establish the appropriate amount of discipline in the pose and cues that are unnecessary, ambiguous, or misleading. We should be especially wary of cues that are designed to direct us toward a pre-defined conclusion. For example, cueing that is too technical or too verbose spoon feeds the asana experience to the student so that there is nothing left for him to discover. If asana practice is too rigidly defined in terms of right and wrong, it will restrict the student's freedom to learn for himself.

Enlighten Your Body

CHAPTER FOURTEEN

Time Management

I no longer sympathize with yoga students who tell me that they don't have enough time in their busy lives to commit to a daily yoga practice, or to eat breakfast, or to get enough sleep, etc. When people say "I don't have time for this," what they are really saying is that they have chosen their priorities and "this" is not one of them. I believe that we can always find time for what we really want to do.

Over-scheduling is the most blatant sign of a life lived without attention to one's priorities. The over-extended individual is a slave to his schedule. He is always aware that the clock is ticking. Living under constant time pressure is stressful. It leaves us unable to perform at our best. The time crunch mentality further deceives us into thinking that our time should only be allocated to activities that result in net gain. We believe that anything else is silly and insignificant – a waste of time.

The time crunch mentality makes us feel like we have no time for leisure activities, no time for rest and relaxation, and certainly no time for moments of stillness and contemplation. If we don't have time to sit down and read a book without feeling guilty, why would we practice yoga asana – whose primarily intrinsic value certainly doesn't result in financial gain or personal glory?

The perception of time pressure has a negative effect on the body. The body prepares itself for constant and hurried activity by increasing its resting tension level. It manifests the physical characteristics of protection – a tightened, compressed abdomen, a shortened neck, a locked jaw, inhibited respiration, heightened dependency on visual and aural input, and oversensitivity. The body is responding to the mental directive to remain on alert. It must be prepared to meet the demands and assaults of the external environment. But living in the shadow of time-related pressure eventually leaves us dissatisfied. On some level of consciousness we feel that we are suffering.

The perception of time pressure complicates our ability to endure the stillness of a yoga pose. When executing a challenging asana, physical discomfort like muscular fatigue is perceived as suffering. Mental discomfort manifests as boredom. Students will come out of the pose when they feel that any form of discomfort is becoming overwhelming.

The real reason they come out of the pose is due to the issue of time. They come out of the pose simply because they don't see an end in sight – *an end to the suffering*. In fact, all they see is suffering. What happens is that the psyche becomes disturbed or distressed in response to a physically demanding situation. If the psyche has not had prior encounters with discomfort or inconvenience, it will not know how to alleviate or manage the body's stress response. When this happens, the challenging physical demands of asana result in psychological breakdown.

Most of us are accustomed to living in a state of comfort. To a certain extent, our familiarity with comfort has made us weak and dependant. When our senses register any sort of challenge or threat, we tend to over-diagnose the severity of the situation. We label even minute states of stress as suffering when words like inconvenience or discomfort provide a more accurate description.

Habituation toward comfort and classifying moderate physical discomfort as unacceptable and unmanageable contribute to the breakdown of the psyche during asana. This sort of breakdown is not the same as the conscious decision to 'let go' and surrender the ego. This sort of breakdown is a form of 'giving up.'

But asana is meant to be a lesson in success, not failure. Therefore, we must choose and manage our yogic challenges appropriately so that we can experience success. When practicing yoga asana, we are placing ourselves in a situation where we will acknowledge the discomfort that we usually seek to avoid. In this way, we are promoting self-improvement by choosing and confronting a psycho-somatic challenge. Our lesson comes from the introspective discoveries that occur when we are faced with a moderately stressful situation *in a controlled and safe environment.*

To meet the challenge, we must be willing to go to our edge – that decisive moment when we must choose between submission and perseverance. We will never experience the point of challenge if we don't come to our edge in the pose, and we won't come to our edge in the pose until we've held the pose long enough to confront the tenacious ego. The question we must resolve is "Who's really in charge? Me, or my ego?"

In a group practice session, students are not in control of the specific duration of the asana. The instructor decides how long they will hold the pose. But the students are always in control of their particular asana experience. This experience includes how much effort to put forth, the specific placement to attain, strategies for sustenance, the psychological focus, and the monitoring of respiration and tension level. This combination of factors determines whether one's perception of the asana experience is positive or negative.

When the mind begins to question the body's endurance capabilities, even the advanced students let themselves become manipulated by time pressure. They allow their minds to wonder "How much time has passed?" or "How much longer must we hold this pose?" Coupled with advancing physical fatigue, such time-related questions plague one's psyche.

We have three choices when dealing with time perception. They include (1) yielding or the avoidance strategy, (2) the psycho-somatic coping strategy, and (3) the cognitive reprogramming strategy.

In the first case, we perceive time as a shackling device that binds, confines, and limits us. The mind says "We've been in this pose a really long time." We begin to wonder how much longer we will have to stay in this pose. The psyche gradually becomes agitated and distressed. Finally it rebels against the asana experience. When this perspective is dominant, we obsess over the negativity of the experience. We entertain thoughts like "This is boring, painful, and worthless," and "My time would be better spent elsewhere."

The second strategy is a psycho-somatic technique in which we soften or modify the impetus to quit. We do this by consciously scanning the body's available resources and shifting energy usage. This is a positive technique that teaches us to actively seek out other options and be willing to switch strategies.

The most constructive coping strategy involves conscious reprogramming of our thoughts. In this strategy, we focus on what our brain is processing. This is a mildly self-hypnotic state in which we consciously choose what to think about and what to disregard. It is also a useful therapy for individuals dealing with an abnormally low pain threshold or the phantom pain phenomenon (pain that is not based on true somatic input).

Cognitive reprogramming can be used to increase our tolerance to discomfort. By focusing on our strengths instead of our weaknesses, conscious reprogramming enables us to persevere when facing a physical or mental challenge.

An excellent example of the cognitive reprogramming strategy involves disciplining ourselves to 'live in the moment.' In this strategy, we consciously bypass time-related worries such as past memories or future projections. The psyche is held steady by the meditative repetition of a neutral, non-intrusive affirmation like "inhale, exhale."

Whatever strategy we choose, our objective is to enhance our ability to persevere. To be effective, the capacity for perseverance should not be conceived in anger, resistance, or force. Calmness and patience in the face of a challenge lead to self-discipline. Self-discipline frees us from being manipulated by the stress of an urgent situation.

The ability to consciously allocate the use of our time, based on the accurate identification of our priorities, is the foundation of the evolutionary process.

Conscious intent refers to the conscious allocation of both our time and our energies. We need to realize that it's O.K. to make time for doing things that we enjoy. These activities are valuable simply because they bring pleasure to our lives. During such moments of pleasure, time seems to be suspended and energy seems to flow from an endless source. But if we believe that outside influences are controlling us, we will feel trapped in a life that lacks pleasure, meaning, or purpose. Without conscious intent, we allow ourselves to be manipulated by a scattered consciousness based on irrelevant distractions.

CHAPTER FIFTEEN

Faith or Fear

There are two reasons that we have difficulty moving forward in life or in asana practice. One is our addiction to comfort. The other is fear. Fear is what makes the first step the hardest. Just as we prepare to go forward, fear of the unknown stops us dead in our tracks.

A few years ago, I went through a period of reoccurring dreams. I kept dreaming that long shards of glass were imbedded into the palms of my hands and the soles of my feet. The glass caused continual aggravation and discomfort. But when I considered the agonizing pain involved in having the glass removed, I wasn't sure I could do it. I wasn't sure I wanted to do it. It seemed to be easier just to keep living with the pain that I had. Even though life wasn't altogether comfortable or happy, at least it was manageable.

Surprisingly enough, in every dream I decided to try to pull out one piece of glass. The beginning of the process was, just as I had anticipated, excruciatingly painful! As I began to tug on the glass (please note that I did the 'pulling out' myself), there was a *moment* of intense pain.

But as soon as the sliver was loose of its lodged position, I knew I could endure. I knew that I could see the process through to conclusion. In the instant when the sliver came all the way out, I experienced absolute relief! I was totally released from the despair, agony, regrets, and pain. I was freed from the chronic low grade misery that I had been living with.

In the dreams, the absence of pain brought a newfound awareness of peace. This non-sensation was a welcome yet unfamiliar experience for me. It was amazing that in one moment I could go from living in pain to living pain-free. Had I known it would be that easy, maybe I would have removed the glass splinters long ago!

These dreams taught me that anticipation of the pain was much worse than the actual pain. The key lesson I learned was that the hardest part is getting started. It takes courage to initiate the process of restoration and renewal. Taking that first step out of the Comfort Zone isn't going to be easy. The thought of leaving the familiar behind is often the most difficult part of the journey.

Here's another example of fear at the beginning of the journey. It also shows how a smidgen of faith can make all the difference: Being a big city girl, I've never been comfortable in the dark or in the woods. On the way to a yoga retreat in rural Georgia, I found myself in the midst of both. I stopped short in my tracks. Like a stubborn mule, I refused to budge. David coaxed me to "come on," but I couldn't take a step. I kept thinking about how dark it was. I kept thinking that we were alone in the woods. I couldn't see anything at all, let alone the path. I kept thinking of all the terrible things that could happen if I stepped forward into the darkness. What if a wild animal attacked my foot? What if I poked my eye out on a sharp tree branch?

Then David said to me, "Hold my hand and take a step." Even though I didn't have faith in the situation, I did have faith in him. So I held his hand and carefully felt my way forward with one foot. The gravel surface seemed unstable. Hesitantly, I took another little step. And then another.

Suddenly, miraculously, the entire sky lit up! I could see the whole path before me! By taking a few little steps, I had moved into a clearing. The moonlight was no longer obstructed by trees, and my surroundings were totally illuminated. Free from fear, I cheerfully trotted along and we made it to the seminar on time.

It is somewhat humorous to think that as I stood frozen in the darkness I was only a few steps away from the light. If I hadn't gathered the courage to go forward, I would not have known how close I was. I would never have reached my destination.

Uncertainty based on fear of the unknown is what held me back. Overcoming uncertainty requires courage. Courage to confront the unknown requires faith. Faith is what replaces fear, for faith and fear cannot coexist.

Reading the Body

During asana, we can actually see or 'read' a person's tendency or preference toward fear or faith. Attitudes are clearly displayed in the language of the body. We can get a feel for a person's strengths and weaknesses by observing his body as he performs different asanas. Even a lack of awareness in a certain body part, as well as the serene or aggressive nature of his personality, is evident during asana.

Let's study the Warrior pose as an example of how we can 'read the body.' When working with yoga students, I am always careful to clarify the peaceful qualities of these Warrior poses. I am not looking to invoke the aggressive impulse that is commonly associated with the term 'warrior.' I remind them that peaceful warriors are thoroughly prepared for battle, but they do not harbor a desire toward hostility or animosity. Neither are they fearful or withdrawn. They do not doubt their abilities. They are willing to stand their ground in battle. They are disciplined, attentive, and able, but they do not actively provoke their adversary. Peaceful warriors exude an air of confidence, courage, and commitment. They believe whole-heartedly that their cause is just.

Figure # 1   Figure # 2   Figure # 3

Study the three pictures of the Warrior stance. The first example shows a warrior who wants to provoke battle. We can see that she has overstepped neutrality, for her chest is thrust forward from the line of the pelvis.

The second example shows a warrior who wants to run from battle. We can tell that she is experiencing inner conflict because she has a sunken, collapsed chest. Her body language indicates retreat or non-commitment.

The third picture shows a warrior who is balanced and whole. Her psyche and soma support and complement each other. We can see that her presence emits the equanimity of the peaceful warrior. To the observer, it is obvious that the each body's attitude matches its intent.

We can even distinguish an individual's unconscious preference toward fear or faith by looking at a specific body part. Study the use of the arms in the three pictures of the next Warrior pose. It's easy to tell which arms lack conscious awareness and which arms are actively engaged.

In the first and second pictures we see arms that lack awareness. In the first picture, notice the lack of a cohesive anatomical line in the fingers, hands, and wrists. This is symbolic of the warrior who goes to battle with the tip of her sword broken or bent. Will she be an effective warrior? Is she adequately prepared?

| Figure # 1 | Figure # 2 | Figure # 3 |
| Droopy hands | Weak arms | Arms are 'alive' |

In the second picture the arms appear weak and disconnected. They look like they lack understanding or intent. But in the third picture we see arms that exude confidence and expression. These arms have almost taken on the appearance of a strong, staff-type combat weapon. These photos are wonderful examples of how a quality of consciousness can permeate the entire body, from core to extremities.

In the case of yoga asana, students lack faith in their abilities for one of two reasons. (1) Some have absolutely no conscious somatic contact with their own anatomy. (2) Others doubt the validity of their own inner wisdom.

Students that lack somatic awareness will experience little or no sensations in their body. Lack of conscious connection to the body requires a coping behavior, such as the withdrawal response or body armoring. Coping behaviors or coping strategies indicate the presence of fear and the absence of faith.

Students that lack faith in their abilities will question the validity of their inner wisdom. They will require affirmation by the instructor. These students need to be accepted. To feel comfortable and confident, they need someone to tell them that they are on the right track.

The yoga student who needs acceptance and approval is living with a degree of fear. He is afraid of being wrong, being punished, or being incompetent. What he fears most is being himself. Deep down inside he believes that he is not good enough. He lacks faith in the world around him, and he lacks faith in himself.

Protective Device # 1: The Winter Coat Consciousness

A person who lacks faith bears an unconscious need for a protective device or a compensation strategy. In an attempt to stay safe and warm in a cold, cold world, the most common coping strategy is the 'winter coat' consciousness. The 'winter coat' is a form of somatic body armor that we put on to protect ourselves.

The heavy 'winter coat' causes the head to drop forward and the shoulders to hunch. The elevated shoulders then collapse inward to close the chest and protect the heart. Psychologically, the 'winter coat' consciousness secures a barrier between one's self and one's surroundings. Relationships are held a safe distance apart.

The cuddly 'winter coat' consciousness is originally put on to carry us through the stress and hardship of an interpersonal or intrapersonal 'cold spell.' But it is easy to become seduced by the artificial ease of comfort and security that it provides. This is why many people continue to wear it - even when the situation has 'warmed up.' We believe that the winter coat is a useful adaptation, maybe even a necessary compensation. Pretty soon wearing the 'winter coat consciousness' has become a familiar, habitual state of being.

It would be hard to do an asana while wearing a big, bulky, winter coat. It would be confining and awkward. It would limit our physical possibilities for the pose. Most of us would agree that it's a good idea to take off the winter coat if we want to move and function with ease. But we're also aware that we've grown fond of and familiar with the 'winter coat consciousness.' So how do we go about removing it?

To remove our 'winter coats,' we must improve the accuracy of our impressions. If we could see through our delusional, erroneous beliefs, we would no longer let assumptions destroy our faith.

Protective Device # 2: Trying too hard

The most common error among yoga students is trying too hard. Of course the flipside also exists – not trying hard enough. But the underachiever consciousness is much less common than the overachiever. Why do students try too hard? They try too hard because they desperately want to succeed. They want to please the instructor. They want and need to be recognized as being right.

Trying too hard often leads to a phenomenon called endgaining, or seeking the goal by any means possible. Endgaining is a strategy used to overcome the assumption of inferiority. The thought process goes like this - "I am wrong, so I will compensate by trying harder to be right."

We have all been indoctrinated to believe that "hard work pays off" and "if I try hard enough, I will succeed." This is the mindset of the person who needs to achieve to prove his worth. But trying too hard often results in frustration or injury. At best, an injury will cause you to postpone or limit your practice. At worst, it will make it so that you cannot practice or function at all.

No Guarantees

What if asana practice came with some sort of prescriptive guarantee? What if you were told that after 356 executions of the shoulderstand your body would be absolutely pain-free? What if you knew it took 400 hours of meditation to reach enlightenment? Would this sure thing be a comforting and motivating factor? For some of us, the answer would be a definite and resounding yes. For others, the effort involved would be too great a task, even with the results guaranteed.

Most of us wholeheartedly understand that asana has the potential to reshape and restore the body's natural structure and health. But the catch is that we do not know how many tiny steps it will take to reach the clearing and come into the light. We have no guarantee of exactly if or when the moments of healing, advancement, revelation, or inspiration will occur. To a certain extent, we must rely on faith.

The first step toward building faith is to commit to the stillness of the body in the pose. Initially, mental dialogue may sound militaristic as you tell yourself, "I am not going to move. I am not going to back out of the pose. I do not allow myself the possibility of an escape hatch. I commit to being perfectly still." A vigilant mode of firmness and discipline is often the best way to get started. This deliberate and well-established mental commitment must exist before the body can truly yield to the pose. This is the only way that you can 'let go' right down to the molecular level of consciousness.

We must commit to being still so that both the psyche and soma completely give up on the possibility of quitting. When we have relinquished the desire to quit, the psyche begins to merge with the soma in asana. Only then might we approach or encounter the blissful state of absolute relaxation. Only then do we begin to release the deepest, tightest, and oldest layers of tension. This is when the inner dialogue evolves into a softer form of affirmation, such as "and still I stay."

Our intent is to unite the psyche and the soma with the common belief that "This is who, what, and where I am, *and I accept it*. I can honestly deal with the fact that *I am*." This deduction cannot be a false or pretend sort of mental acceptance. Habitual fear is relinquished only when you are absolutely free from lingering doubt. Faith involves the most sincere effort that we are capable of. We must believe to the core of our being – because the body can tell the difference! The soma knows when the psyche deceives, even if it is trying to deceive itself.

❖ Inquiry # 18: "Facing the fear of falling"

Concept: The bottom line is that our own cognition can limit the asana experience by provoking our fears. Let's try, right now, to face those fears. Try to perform the single leg standing balance pose that you see pictured here.

Inquiry # 18: "Facing the fear of falling"

Ask yourself, "What's the worst that can happen?" As far as the psyche is concerned, the worst that can happen is death for the ego fears its own demise. The question to address at this time is "When I attempt this yoga pose, what am I afraid of?" You are certainly not going to die in the pose. The worst that can happen is that you lose your balance and put your hands or your back foot down. Then you can try again. Or not. It's your choice. On the scale of life challenges, this is not a big deal. Keep the pose in perspective. Keep the faith. Remember your priorities.

Faith gives us the freedom to choose. As we enter into the asana challenge, we choose our perception and we choose our responses. The result is that we have chosen our experience. In so doing, we have declared our own version of reality.

CHAPTER SIXTEEN

Limitations to Freedom

I didn't truly experience conscious awareness in my hands until I studied a form of classical Indian dance called Bharatanatyam. As a youngster I had participated in ballet, cheerleading, and gymnastics, so I assumed that I was coordinated enough to handle Bharatanatyam's gesture work without difficulty. But the intensity, variety, and abundance of the hand and finger configurations in this dance form was unimaginable!

I was obviously awkward, clumsy, and inept. I felt personally inadequate. The challenge to improve the dexterity of my hands was almost overwhelming, mostly because I considered some of these intricate gestures to be virtually impossible. I often wanted to quit.

The truth is that I didn't know what my hands were actually capable of - *because I wasn't aware of what was possible.* Looking back, I now realize that my frustration was largely due to the novelty of this sensori-motor experience. I was stuck in the uncomfortable and unfulfilling stage of Conscious Incompetence for quite some time, for Bharatanatyam's gestures totally contradicted my current level of knowledge and expertise regarding my hands. But with a lot of practice (and a few tears), I was thrilled to discover that my hands were capable of development that I had never dreamed of.

This experience taught me that our subconscious psychological parameters can curtail our physical possibilities. Because these parameters are subconscious, our conscious minds aren't aware of them. Unfortunately, many people live a lifetime not knowing that they have pre-determined their own potential by believing in certain limitations.

Our mistake is our limited scope. We are often amazed that our bodies and minds are more capable than we had originally thought. We are surprised to discover that we ourselves have placed limitations on the experience of freedom.

Freedom means being at liberty. When we are free, we are not bound, constrained, or confined. Freedom is a state of being in which we are unobstructed and clear. These terms are significant in the understanding of freedom, because they imply openness, availability, and a capacity to respond in a spontaneous and natural manner. The state of freedom is not defined by pre-conceived notions. Freedom supersedes the human tendency toward habituation by past learning.

When we realize this, we are truly free to 'have the experience' of a lifetime - complete with personal choice, self-expression, responsibility, and creativity. 'Having the experience' refers to the state of mind-body unity as it occurs in the present timeframe. 'Having the experience' means honoring your personal perceptions and natural reactions.

'Having the experience' is all about being your self. It is the ultimate manifestation of the Participant-consciousness. The self participates totally and completely in the particular circumstances and relationships. 'Having the experience' is playing an active part in the experience without needing to analyze, judge, interpret, or premeditate.

Cognitive Habits

Certain cognitive habits limit our ability to fully immerse ourselves into the Participant-consciousness that is necessary if we want to 'have the experience.' Cognitive habits, though useful continuity devices, are pernicious creatures that confine and control our movements. They limit our potential. The specific cognitive processes that act as limitation devices include memory, projection, judgment, desire, and future dreams.

Memories are recollections of one's past performance, abilities, and experiences. These recollections are based on one's perceptions of the past performance, abilities, and experiences. Example: "My knees used to hurt during that pose."

Projections are speculation about one's future performances, abilities, and experiences. These speculations are based on one's past performances, abilities, and experiences. Example: "That pose is going to hurt my knees."

Judgments are opinions or discriminating appraisals that are held with confidence but are not substantiated by proof. Example: "My knees hurt in that pose because I have bad knees" or "That pose is a bad pose because it hurts my knees."

Desires are attachment to, as well as hope for, the possible realization of a predefined or pre-established expectation. Example: "I really want to do that pose without my knees hurting."

Future dreams are contemplations pertaining to occurrences that are yet to occur. Future dreams can act as a positive, motivating force or they can be another limiting device. If based on unrealistic perceptions or inaccurate information, future dreams fall into the category of limitation device. If they are based on realistic data and sufficient resources or talent, they will be positive and motivating. Example: "Maybe my knees won't hurt when I do the pose next time."

At first, all yoga students think in terms of limitations or superlatives. An example of limitation thinking is "I can't do that pose because I'm 44 years old." The implication is that age is a limiting factor. The flipside of the limited "this is as far as I can go" consciousness is the superlative "this is what I have to do, what I have to attain, what I must be" consciousness. An example of superlative thinking during the seated forward fold pose would be "I have to keep my legs straight" or "I have to touch my head to my knees (or to my feet)," or even a self-flagellating statement like "I should be doing better than this."

The tendency toward superlative thinking comes from the competitive urge. It is often sparked by seeing the ultimate execution of a pose in a book or from watching an accomplished teacher demonstrate the finished pose. Superlatives are a limitation device that diminishes our perception of self worth. When we think in terms of superlatives, we are often setting ourselves up for failure by embracing a standard that is unreal or out of reach.

The content of our verbal interactions with others can also yield a positive or a negative effect on our psyches. For example, the yoga instructor who imposes negative value judgments as part of her cueing technique is neither helpful nor beneficial to her students. "You can do better than this" or "You have horrible posture" are meant to tear the student down. These statements zero in on the student's weaknesses or flaws and put them on public display.

I strongly suggest that you disregard any demeaning comments made by this sort of instructor. Furthermore, if the instructor never offers any form of warmth, praise, encouragement, or support, you should harbor no doubts about leaving the class. Find a kinder, gentler instructor who supports her students' process of somatic re-education by providing a safe, nurturing environment that is rich with positive feedback and camaraderie. A sincere, self-respecting yoga instructor would never intentionally damage a student's confidence and self-image by belittling his abilities.

Non-judgment

None of us is in the position to judge the experience of another person or of our selves. Instead of judgment, we should think in terms of validation. In its own way, each and every experience is valid. Here's an example of what I mean:

Occasionally when I practice savasana (the corpse pose) during final relaxation I have the experience of my body dissolving into a small cloud of dust that hovers a few inches above the floor. A few times I have fallen asleep during savasana. I have also had such a severe backache that I was never able to truly relax. My most common experience during savasana is a generic state of relaxation that is unremarkable yet satisfying. Of all these different types of savasana experiences, the dust cloud is certainly the most mystical! But in its own way, a brief catnap is also highly satisfying. The nagging backache, though not a fun or serene experience, informs me that my body is not prepared for a day of hearty exertion.

The moral is that one experience is not better, more rewarding, or more valuable than another. The important thing is being consciously present so that we can have the experience *that is appropriate for us in this particular moment.* We need not evaluate its worth, for this information is usually beyond our level of comprehension. Judgment and comparison don't belong in the practice of yoga asana.

Asana training provides the time and place to practice releasing negative thought patterns and replacing them with non-delusional affirmations. Though asana looks like a purely physical practice, it actually provides a wonderful opportunity to clear the psyche. With a lot of practice (and possibly a little luck) the positive ways of thinking that has been tried and tested during asana practice will carry over into our everyday life.

Over time, the yoga student realizes that life, like asana, is about more than just the appearance of his actions. He knows that an accurate perspective on life includes an understanding of what he does, how he does it, and why he does it. It includes knowing that the consequences of his thoughts and actions do matter. He understands that it takes a stronger person to correct his mistakes than to deny them.

Accomplishment comes when the student is no longer a slave to his bad habits. The accomplished student no longer makes choices based on guilt, greed, ambition, or competition. He is no longer influenced by shame or pride. He practices asana and chooses his daily activities simply because they feel like the right and reasonable thing to do. He has arrived at the avenue of pure and virtuous intent. The time is right for this yoga student to progress toward a personal daily yoga practice.

At some point, the self-motivated individual will prefer a solitary asana practice. He might find that he no longer requires direction from an instructor and has no real need of support from fellow members of the group. The self-motivated yoga practitioner dwells in the freedom that comes from having faith in the self. A personal practice indicates that a practitioner has dedicated his life to the course of self-discovery. It shows that he is interested in integrating his discoveries into the re-creation of the self. When the time is right, a personal practice will seem more like a gift than a chore.

Enlighten Your Body

PART FOUR
Embodying Wholeness

There are times when the silence and solitude of the Observer are necessary. There are times when the interactions and involvement of the Participant are necessary. But the final step in somatic learning is the merging of the two aspects of consciousness. The Participant must process, assimilate, and apply the informative insights that the Observer has supplied. It is the Participant's responsibility to install appropriate changes in the self that reflect what has been learned.

Integration of the Observer and the Participant is represented in the body as a balance between the abilities of strength and flexibility. It is depicted in the psyche as the attributes of equilibrium and equanimity, coupled with the ability to successfully adapt. When we display these characteristics, we are embodying wholeness.

Enlighten Your Body

CHAPTER SEVENTEEN

Problem Solving

When I was growing up, my parents solved all of my problems for me. No matter what happened, they were always there to pick me up, dust me off, and send me back on my way. I know that I was very fortunate to have such loving parents who cared deeply about my welfare. But a part of me wonders if I was a little too sheltered for my own good.

As a young adult, I didn't know very much about the details of daily life. I had grown to be dependant upon other people for just about everything. My interpersonal skills were inadequate, and I didn't know how to rationally deal with any form of adversity or authority. I had never learned the art of compromise and I had never developed the skills associated with independence.

You can imagine my surprise when I got married and my husband considered me to be his equal. He thought of me as his partner, not his ward. He was my husband, not my surrogate father. It didn't take long for me to figure out that there were certain spousal expectations involved in the marriage situation. For starters, I was part of a committed relationship. I was expected to manage a household, to partake in decision making, and to *cook!*

You might think that these are pretty ordinary tasks that everyone should be able to do. But I'd had no training. None. I seemed to be ill prepared for real life. During the early years of marriage, I hoped David wouldn't find out that I couldn't do anything particularly well.

Feeling incompetent is a terrible thing. You feel useless, unskilled, and unprepared. How could I be a good wife, mother, teacher, cook, dog owner, or anything? I didn't know how to solve any sort of problem. I didn't know how to look at a situation from the other person's perspective. I had never learned how to negotiate. I was used to getting my own way. And I boldly assumed I was always right. (The truth is that I married my husband because I suspected that he was more 'right' than I was!)

I think that a lot of us have found ourselves in a similar situation. One day we wake up and realize that there's a lot of stuff we don't know. If there's a situation that needs to be handled or something that needs to be fixed, we don't know how to do it. We weren't brought up to be effective problem solvers. But problem solving is a practical skill that can be learned. I know this because, over the past fifteen years of marriage, I've learned to be very good at solving problems.

Whenever David went out of town, there was always some sort of crisis on the home front. Looking back, I'm pretty sure that this was the universe's way of teaching me to be responsible. It started with car trouble. I had a lot of car trouble. I had two flat tires and there were four times that my car wouldn't start. Then there were the dog problems. About ten years ago one of our dogs was hit by a dump truck *and survived!* (He's still doing fine.) Last year, one of our other dogs *died* – but just for a little while.

It was summer, and David was in California at a business meeting. The kids and the dogs and I were relaxing out in the sun by our little pool. (I have two kids, three beautiful barking shelties, and a very active dappled dachshund.) It was about 88 degrees with a gentle breeze. This is quite pleasant weather, considering that Tennessee's average summer temperature climbs to 95 with high humidity. It was a perfect summer day, not too hot, not too humid. Though I didn't think about it at the time, later I would remember that two of my friends' dogs had recently died of heat stroke.

After an hour or so, we gathered our towels to go inside. The kids went on ahead while I called to the dogs. The four of them were having fun running around in the yard, but I could tell they looked tired and thirsty. Three dogs came running for the house. I watched as the fourth dog, a sheltie named Arthur, tripped. He lost his balance and fell. He stood up and then fell again. This time he didn't get up. His hind legs began to spasm. My mind screamed "heat stroke!" It was an emergency.

I grabbed the dog and ran for the house. It was much cooler inside the house, but Arthur was already in bad shape. I put him on the doggie bed in the sunroom and called to Jennifer to get a big cup of cool water. I scooped handfuls of water over the dog's head and neck. He was panting heavily. His legs were still shaking and he wasn't even trying to get up. Then the unthinkable happened. He stopped moving and he stopped breathing.

Mentally, I zeroed in on the dog. I remember thinking that the dog could die. But I also remember that I never thought he was going to die. I just thought about being with him, being calm, being in the moment. If this was his time to die, then he would. If not, he would be OK. Either way, I knew I could handle it. I also knew that the kids and the other dogs would take their cues from how I behaved.

Then one of the other shelties did the strangest thing. It was April, our only female dog. She's the dog that I can always count on to be responsible. When there's a problem in the dog world, she takes care of it. She has proven herself as the peacekeeper, the nurse, the mother, the sentry, the huntress, and the babysitter. Suddenly, in the midst of this crisis, she lay down and fell asleep. No kidding! She positioned herself tail to tail with the comatose dog and went to sleep. Deep sleep.

I'm not sure if I witnessed a mystical dog-to-dog healing or not, but in less than a minute Arthur came back to life. He started panting heavily, but he was calm. He appeared to be peaceful and relaxed. I was pretty sure he was going to survive. We, the humans, stayed with him while he lay there for another twenty minutes. Slowly, he managed to stand up. He walked to the kitchen and drank a bowl full of water. He seemed to have recovered from his near-death experience. April also woke up. The crisis was over and the story had a happy ending.

I've learned that solving problems doesn't have to be particularly grueling. It's really pretty simple. Here's what you do: (1) If possible, be prepared. (2) Stay calm. (3) Do the best you can.

There's one more thing you can do to alleviate your problems. You can change your expectations. If something doesn't meet our expectations, we call it a problem. If we didn't have a lot of expectations, right away we'd decrease our potential for problems. Instead of being 'problems,' the things that happen would just be 'things that happen.' No big deal. Nothing to get upset over.

Seeking Options

As much as I like the phrase 'mind over matter,' sometimes I think it would be best if we forgot all about it. Instead of thinking in terms of 'mind controlling matter,' let's give our bodies the recognition they deserve! When the body and mind share an equal partnership - a sort of spousal relationship - problems are more easily overcome. Effective cognition and responsible behaviors are the result of a mind and body working together in harmony.

Yoga asana helps us re-establish psycho-somatic harmony. Asana also teaches us to be good problem solvers. This mind-body method teaches us how to adapt. It teaches us how to employ a synergy of skills and wisdom. Skills include the specific psycho-somatic techniques that we have been learning. Wisdom refers to the ability to access knowledge, to apply common sense and good judgment, and to be creative when applying the techniques. This means actively seeking other options – being on the lookout for new ways of doing things.

Yoga teaches us the art of creative compromise. In yoga asana, we monitor our bodies and our minds so that we can recognize a problem as soon as it arises. If we attend to a problem before it becomes a full blown crisis, we have a better chance of maintaining our discipline and our confidence. We have a better chance of persevering. Problem solving teaches us to carry on in spite of temporary obstacles. It teaches us to do the best we can, given what we have to work with.

When we practice yoga asana, we take on a physical and mental challenge. Every asana presents some sort of problem, whether simple or complex, that we must solve. For example, let's look at what happens during a pose in which the arm position becomes a problem. As moments pass, the average student entertains thoughts of insufficiency. These thoughts are provoked by fatigue in the musculature that suspends the arms. At the periphery of his consciousness, the student senses that his discipline is beginning to waver. As physical discomfort increases, the student perceives the arms as becoming critically demanding. The whole structure of the pose itself seems more difficult.

Mental energy withdraws from much of the body so that it can be redirected toward the arms. The student suspects that the pose might become painful or even impossible. This future projection is what leads to probable or eventual failure. Negative thoughts contribute to the gradual dissolution of the student's tenacity. Once he has opened the door to mental negativity, his ability to maintain equanimity comes into question. At this point the student's capacity for conscious control and logical coping is disturbed. The steady state of the psyche has become distracted. When the psyche switches from functioning via faith to functioning via fear, it's likely that the student will soon submit to both psychological and somatic defeat.

❖ Inquiry # 19: "Proper Carriage of the Arms"

Concept: In this inquiry we experience the sensation of good arm carriage.

Discussion: Good arm carriage is an invaluable skill that many of us lack. In spite of this, our arms and our bodies seem to function just fine. We can pick things up. We can open doors. We can do our jobs. Poor arm carriage isn't necessarily a big problem. But it is a little problem. And there is a better option. Improving our arm carriage might save us from a future injury or chronic pain. If we solve the little problem now, it need never become a big crisis. This lesson teaches us that good use of a single body part directly affects the body-as-a-whole.

Directions: You may perform this inquiry standing or sitting. Follow the four cues.

Inquiry # 19:
"Proper carriage of the arms"

1. With the arms hanging at your sides, externally rotate the shoulders so that the palms face out.

2. Slowly lift the arms to shoulder height, keeping the shoulders pressed down. Try to position the arms so that the tips of the middle fingers are as far apart as possible.

3. Notice the position (and sensation) of the scapula in your back.

4. Maintain that sensation as you slowly turn the palms down.

❖ Inquiry # 20: "Sustaining Integration in the Arms"

Concept: In this inquiry, we will try to solve the problem of experiencing fatigue in the arms. We'll examine different strategies for coping and sustaining integration. We'll see how good use in all body parts directly affects our asana experience.

Directions: Recreate these arm positions. Hold each position for ten steady breaths or one to two minutes. Notice which pose is easiest and which is hardest. Which muscles got fatigued? Which body parts ached? What made you want to quit the pose?

Inquiry # 20:
"Sustaining Integration in the arms"

Chair Pose   Warrior Two

Discussion: Different arm positions require different coping strategies. In the two poses pictured above, we see two different arm positions. Each pose represents a different challenge for suspending the arms, and each pose requires a different solution.

In terms of the arms, there are two reasons why the Chair pose should be the easiest. The first reason is because the arms are held close to the body. The second reason is that the diagonal positioning of the spinal column is not too far from vertical. The arms in the Warrior Two pose presents a greater challenge because the arms are spread farther away from the body's center line. This creates a long lever that is much more difficult to suspend.

A common pattern of misuse in the Chair pose is the tendency to hang the arms from the trapezius muscle and bunch up the neck. The best solution is to attend to the following cues "Keep the shoulders down as the arms lift up," and "release and lengthen the neck." Tight pectoralis and anterior deltoid muscles need to be stretched. The rhomboids, the lower trapezius, and the latissimus dorsi muscles need to be strengthened. It helps to picture an anatomical line from the armpit through the pinkie finger. Remember, the palms should be facing each other, and the shoulders should be rolled down and back.

Another pattern of misuse is a lack of stability in the base of support. The Chair pose is a standing pose, so the feet are the base of support. But the diagonal position of the spinal column requires a redistribution of the body's weight. Squeezing the inner knees together supplements the body's stability. This inward pressing action anchors the body in the pose. It balances, distributes, and redirects the body's weight downward into the feet. Attention to the base of support is always an important energy-conservation strategy that helps us endure the pose.

Let's look at the details of the arm placement in the other pose. In Warrior Two, the position of the head relative to the neck, and the position of the neck relative to the torso make all the difference between pain and prosperity. Again, we should not allow the arms to hang from the trapezius. Instead, the weight of the arms needs to be supported by proper placement of the scapula (see Inquiry # 19). We should avoid obsessing over the sensations experienced in the shoulders, chest, and mid-back. Anytime you lock your thoughts on an area of the body, the tension level in that area rises. Fanatic cognition produces physical tension.

It would be better to bring your awareness to the tips of the middle fingers. This visualization encourages ease of extension and expansion. The soma gets the affirmative message that "It's O.K. for me to be this big. It's O.K. for me to expand to my full potential." Given good technique and the ability to solve problems creatively, it's amazing what a person can do!

Last but not least, there is a simple but powerful problem solving strategy called visualization. Visualization is beneficial because *how we see things in our minds is how we create our version of reality.* Let's test this theory by re-examining the arms in the Warrior II pose (from Inquiry # 20). Let's see if we can use visualization to enhance the experience.

Most people think of the shoulder and wrist as the boundaries of the arm. But what if we were to focus on the qualities of length and extension in the arms? What if we visualize the arms as being anchored in the heart? This image completely changes our perspective. The arms are no longer perceived as random or separate body parts. Instead, they contribute to an interrelated whole. This visualization lightens and lengthens our perception of the arms. They seem to float upward or outward from the body's core.

Metaphorically, arms that extend from the heart symbolize purity of intent. Our arms are *connected* to our hearts. As we reach out to make contact with the world around us, we express what is in our hearts. By using visualization, we have produced lightness of being and lightness of attitude.

As our attitude lightens, it shifts toward enlightenment - and our outlook becomes more positive. A positive outlook makes a major contribution toward our ability to sustain integration. Both the pose and our lives get a lot easier when we stop obsessing about what's wrong and start noticing the things we are doing right.

The psychological condition called pronoia is a subjective state in which an individual presupposes a positive outcome. By adapting the attitude of pronoia (the opposite of paranoia), we assume that everything is working in our best interest. Again, our problem load is automatically reduced.

Problem solving and maintenance skills help clear the rubbish of past regrets from our path. They are compulsory features of the adult consciousness. When I told my children that a big part of being an adult involves problem solving and maintenance, they said that being an adult sounds boring.

This immediately reminded me of the time I complained to a friend about much the same thing. I was telling her how I dread and despise the monotonous, time-consuming tasks of running a small business. Being a small business owner herself, I was sure she would agree. But her perky response that "business is fun" surprised me. It reinforced the notion that fun is a state of mind. Fun need not be contingent upon liberation from duty. You can have fun even when solving problems.

Business, asana, and life are obviously fun when they provide freedom. It's fun to be creative. It's fun to be successful and to earn money. It's fun when things turn out the way you want them to. It's fun when you get your way. But the responsible adult also finds satisfaction in managing the necessary prerequisites and duties of daily life. The ordinary chores and simple tasks that satisfy our fundamental needs really aren't so bad. They're really not problems at all.

CHAPTER EIGHTEEN
Progression

Do you remember that old saying, "Be careful what you wish for, because you just might get it?" Last year, I was slapped in the face with the reality of this statement.

Life had become busier than usual. The kids were going to different schools, so we left the house every morning at 7:00 AM and I drove for about forty minutes. To make matters worse, almost every day there were a couple of food items that we desperately needed. This meant that I had to swing by the grocery store after dropping the kids at their schools. Luckily my favorite market was a couple miles down the road from Paul's school. So the detour for groceries wasn't too much out of the way. But I considered it an additional early morning *chore.*

One day I was complaining to David about the inconvenience of having to stop at the grocery store every day. As the words tumbled out of my mouth, I was awestruck by a strange coincidence. In that instant, I remembered what I had tentatively planned for our future retirement. When we retired, I wanted to go to the grocery store early every morning to buy fresh produce. I would purchase the particular things that I needed for that day. This was part of my plan for relaxation and nourishment in our golden years. The irony was unmistakable! Even though we hadn't retired, the universe had granted my wish. *So why was I complaining?*

I felt so sheepish. I immediately adjusted my attitude regarding the early morning visits to the grocery store. I began to enjoy them. I looked forward to them. I embraced the fact that going to the grocery store was part of my everyday schedule. I chatted with all of the early morning employees. I laughed every time the dachshund stuck his snout into the bags to get a sniff of what I had brought home.

The two morals to the story are (1) wish carefully, and (2) the universe supports you!

Embodying health

Many of us have unknowingly grown accustomed to our ailments. We are used to living in a somewhat incapacitated or unfulfilled state which we assume is permanent. Furthermore, many of us define ourselves by our ailments, traumas, and transgressions. We wear them like a badge of honor. Our bodies and our subconscious tendencies say to the world, "I am fragile, so you should feel sorry for me. I had a difficult childhood, so

you should forgive me. I am wounded, so you should take care of me."
But what happens when past ailments and bad habits are cleared?

When our 'regrets' are ameliorated, we can no longer hide behind
them. We can no longer rely on them to conceal our improprieties and
deficiencies. We can no longer use them to excuse ourselves from our
duties. If we are used to playing the role of a victim, this is a big lesson
in reality!

To become wholly healed, we need to let go of any form of victim
consciousness. We do this by integrating the concept of health into our
psyches and somas. But we cannot establish the self-perception of a
healthy person until we accept complete responsibility for our selves and
our lives. We must learn or relearn how to function as happy, healthy,
and responsible individuals.

When we begin practicing yoga, in essence we are telling the
universe that we want to improve ourselves. Many of us are consciously
or unconsciously wishing to clear our past regrets. As we progress in our
study of yoga, we will certainly experience positive changes. The catch
is that we have to figure out what to do with these physical, mental,
emotional, and spiritual changes. Do we accept them or do we throw
them back? Do we embrace them or will they become something else to
complain about? What will we do when our wish is fulfilled?

I find it interesting to look back on how yoga has changed my
students. I enjoy observing what they have done with their
transformation. At the very least, most students got more relaxed in their
bodies and in their attitudes. Many told me that their relationships had
improved. Almost everyone was more content and felt like they had
learned to enjoy life.

Occasionally there was a student who decided that yoga was exactly
what he or she needs. These students became teachers. In the past nine
years, I've had seven students become yoga teachers. Just like me, these
individuals had an inherent need to learn the lessons of yoga very, very
well. The unspoken motto of the yoga teacher is "I teach, therefore I
learn." Whether we call ourselves a yoga teacher or a yoga student, we
are all students.

Every now and then there was a student who couldn't get past the old
traumas, injuries, and imbedded habits. On some level of consciousness,
he had come to rely on a dramatic existence based on histrionic
behaviors, volatile relationships, and irrational cognition. Remarkably, I
have seen some very 'lost' students change their core beliefs so that they

could progress. But there were others who couldn't or wouldn't identify, accept, and address negativities in their selves. Eventually, these students decided that (for one reason or another) yoga was not good for them, and they quit. It's understandable. At one time or another, just about every one of us wrestles with the desire to quit. We want to quit because, for the first time in our lives, the Observer-consciousness lets us *see the self as it is – not as we assume it is, or as we want it to be . . .* and we may not like what we see.

As the Observer-consciousness becomes more discerning, the Participant-consciousness can no longer deny, repress, or falsify its findings. If integration is to be successful, the Participant must begin to invoke positive changes that reflect what has been learned. Be aware that this process cannot be hurried. It will not happen overnight. To make steady progress in our yoga practice, the Participant needs to determine 'how much' and 'how soon.'

Expansion and Contraction

Many schools of yoga classify asana as a preparatory stage for the more advanced esoteric practices. But it is possible for asana to comprise a spiritual path that is comprehensive and efficacious in its own right.

A dedicated asana practice makes our bodies fit and firm, free of disease, and lithe of limb. It helps restore health and harmony to our lives. It neutralizes habitual tendencies toward anxiety or sloth. Through asana, we learn to navigate both the anticipated and the unforeseen tides of change. We learn to implement energetic adaptations of appropriate form and degree. But we need to be able to identify when to act and when not to. We need to determine how much or how hard to push, and when to back off and coast.

At any given moment, we have the choice to direct the flow of our life energy toward expansion (increase) or contraction (decrease). These terms should not be thought of in terms of good and bad. They are actually complementary forces that provide balance and support steady progress. [Perhaps it would be better to use the terms exertion and recuperation.] At the right time and in the right circumstances, both expansion and contraction can be considered positive. Negative consequences result only when one force becomes far too dominant.

The expansive force is tempered and stabilized by the force of contraction. The expansive force is the will to do, and creative discovery is its expression. The expansive force asks "Can it be done?" Contraction counters with "Why do it?" or "Is it appropriate?"

Expansion is fueled by novelty-seeking behaviors and possibility thinking. The contractile force is activated by the need for sustenance, continuity, and the assurance of well-being. Expansion is the raw drive to push onward no matter what. Contraction is the reining force which considers intentions and consequences. Contraction keeps the explosive urge toward expansion in check. The contractile force encourages patience, deeper understanding, and intelligent awareness.

Positive characteristics of the expansive state include opening toward relationship, interest in learning, conscious desire for self-improvement, a positive attitude, seeking and exploring, active maintenance, and other desires. Contraction prefers the status quo. Contraction is the steady state that is quite content with life in the confines of the comfort zone. Contraction draws us back toward safety and security. In the balanced state, the force of expansion slightly exceeds contraction. In this way we experience steady growth through moderation. We are not driven and we are not burdened by stress. A balance life is perceived as being interesting, meaningful, joyous, and fun.

Extreme expansion will have negative manifestations such as risk-taking behaviors, arrogance, emphasizing the self at the expense of others, a reduction in sensitivity, and a lack of integrity. People caught up in superfluous expansive activity can't turn off the ceaseless mental chatter. They will have a hard time keeping the body still and relaxed during asana.

The inability to collect and organize one's thoughts is the mental dilemma of extreme contraction. Physical problems include fatigue and weakness. You might be confused, angry, or hopeless. You might be totally cut off from your feelings. Extreme contraction is characterized by stagnation, self-abuse or addictions (inappropriate desires), seclusion (closing off from relationship), fearfulness, and depression.

Expansive and contractive forces also manifest in the physical body. Contraction produces a pulling inward, a tightening of muscles and compression of the spinal column. Too much contraction restricts the flow of the life force. Narrowing of blood vessels, tension headaches, muscle aches, and fatigue are all examples of excessive somatic contraction.

Though extreme contraction appears to have a detrimental affect on our health, a moderate amount of contraction actually performs a necessary duty. The contractile force acts as a stabilizer.

Without contraction to keep expansion in check, the muscles, organs, and spinal column would lose their integrity. Tension, fatigue, anxiety, or overuse produces unbridled, misdirected energy. Extreme expansion, if left unchecked, will eventually result in some sort of bodily burnout. The systems of the body will gradually begin to break down, with the weakest link being the first to show signs of damage.

Both extreme expansion and extreme contraction waste valuable energy. Extreme expansion demands more energy than is needed or available. It doesn't allow recuperation for restoration. Extreme contraction uses less energy than is needed, but it leaves available energy trapped and congested. This trapped energy will need to find an outlet or it will be deposited somewhere in the body.

The body builder is an example of the physical manifestation of extreme expansion. His goal is to develop bigger than average musculature, perhaps for purposes of strength or an appealing physique. Yet overdevelopment produces other problems such as a lack of flexibility, reduced functional capacity, overemphasis on appearance, and an inflated ego.

The aimless, sluggish 'couch potato' consciousness is an example of extreme contraction. His goal is to restrict activity and interaction. Perhaps this behavior is an avoidance strategy driven by low self esteem. The peaceful couch potato personality has a different set of problems such as overweight, loneliness, boredom, or depression.

❖ Inquiry # 21: "Experiencing Expansion and Contraction"

Concept: In this inquiry, we experience the principles of expansion and contraction in our bodies during asana.

Directions: Try each of the poses pictured for the inquiries. Commit to stillness and silence in each pose for at least one minute. Let your body and mind merge into a somatic understanding regarding the concepts of expansion and / or contraction.

❖ Inquiry # 21a: "Contraction"

A good example of the contractive force is found in the child's pose or the folded plough pose. Observing each pose, we can see the inward-moving contractive influence in the rounded body shape which surrounds and contains the center. As we participate in the pose, we can feel the contractive force pulling us inward toward the core.

Inquiry # 21a: "Contraction"

child's pose

plough pose

❖ Inquiry # 21b: "Expansion"

The triangle pose and the half moon pose are good examples of the expansive force. The concept of expansion is both seen and felt in these poses. The limbs become linear protrusions that extend outward from the core.

Inquiry # 21b: "Expansion"

triangle pose

half moon pose

❖ Inquiry # 21c: "Duality"

There are also poses in which both principles coexist, such as the seated forward fold pose and the half wheel pose. In seated forward fold, the body experiences the state of extension or expansion along the posterior side while also experiencing an anterior contraction. The half wheel pose demonstrates the opposite configuration – an opening or expansion of the body's front side with a simultaneous contraction of the back side.

Inquiry # 21c: "Duality"

seated forward fold pose   half wheel pose

When the opposing forces of contraction and expansion are balanced, a pose is performed with equanimity. The pose is effortless. Initially, the soma responds to the interfacing of these forces by fluctuating back and forth between the feelings of weightiness and weightlessness. The soma feels very heavy and deeply relaxed as it experiences the sensation of sinking. This is the sensation of contraction. Then it feels light and airy as it experiences the sensation of floating. Weightlessness, or lightness-of-being, is the somatic sensation of expansion.

At first consciousness alternates between these diametrically opposed bodily sensations. We feel one and then we feel the other. But the moment that we connect with a true balance of the two forces, the soma registers an absolute absence of sensation.

Enlighten Your Body

CHAPTER NINETEEN

Balance

A lot of yoga asanas require balance. There are standing balances, arm balances, seated balances, and head stands. Even in prone poses like the bow we balance on the front of the pelvis and the ribcage.

In asana, balance is my specialty. I used to say that I could do a series of single leg standing balance poses while perched on top of a telephone pole. Standing on one foot, I can easily perform eight or nine different positions without blinking an eye. I have no problem moving from one pose to the next without any fear of falling. I like balance poses because I have confidence in my ability to balance. I understand what balance is all about, so it doesn't bother me.

I don't think most yoga students share my fondness for balance poses. And I'm not sure it's a coincidence that there's always someone who has to go to the restroom when I introduce a challenging balance pose. A lot of students shy away from the notion of balance. Students are afraid of balance poses because they see them in terms of black or white, right or wrong. They think that finding balance is like looking for a needle in a haystack. They know it's there somewhere, but it's going to be very hard – if not impossible – to find!

The problem is that students are unsure of their abilities to find and maintain balance. They don't know what would lead them to a state of balance. They don't know where or how to find it. They're not sure exactly what they are seeking, or how to recognize it. And even in those fleeting moments when the student does wander into the state of balance, it soon vanishes - despite his most sincere or frantic effort. The extraordinary truth about balance is revealed! *Balance always seems to slip away most quickly when we try too hard to hold it.*

But balance need not be a nearly impossible task. It's not really that hard to find or to sustain. I repeatedly tell my students that "balance is easier than you think it is, because balance is not just a single point." Every pose has a certain acceptable range of adequate balance.

There are two key ideas to remember about balance. First, *balance is a somatic sensation.* Balance is a perception felt within the soma. Second, *balance is not static.* It is constantly changing. Therefore, balance is a constant re-adjustment. The steady state of balance requires vigilant attention (tempered by a detached attitude) to the task at hand.

A Subjective State

To an outside observer, you might look like you're in a steady state of balance. You might appear serene and in control. But on the inside you might be struggling to maintain the external image. Deep inside, you're wrestling with issues of composure and stress.

Being balanced, like being 'centered,' is something that you determine for yourself. Balance is unique to the individual and specific to the moment. It's not something someone else can determine for you. It's a subjective and personal experience. What constitutes acceptable balance for you will change as you progress in your understanding. But you will always know that you have found true balance when you attain a feeling of effortless effort.

As we come to understand what is meant by the concept of balance, we'll see that even our normal two-footed stance requires balance. Sitting on a chair requires balance. Lying on the floor requires balance. Of course these positions offer a much greater margin for error than the stereotypical balance poses. Eventually we'll see that every body position requires a degree of balance. And we'll understand that our bodies benefit from balance that is consciously controlled.

Conscious balance is intelligent balance. It is the result of thoughtful choice regarding the body's use. The primary physical goal in intelligent balance strategies is to maintain alignment while reducing effort. When effort is diminished, energy is conserved and tension is reduced. When we are balanced, the body feels comfortable and casual.

I have noticed that as a student's balance improves, his self-confidence blossoms. Physical balance complements psychological balance. Composure and equilibrium go hand in hand. Affirmations that facilitate the significant victory of attaining one's balance include the following:

"I am not afraid."   Feeling stronger and able. Confidence in one's self and in one's abilities is restored.

"I can choose wisely."   Acceptance of own responsibilities. Accurate perception of one's capabilities. Commitment to personal ethics.

"I can go with the flow." Able to relinquish the need to control. Release of habitual rigidity. The non-judgmental nature emerges. Reacts to the present moment as it unfolds.

Making Connections

In yoga asana, balance is produced by body parts working together in harmony. It's about successful relationships between the parts. It's about making connections. To somatically experience the concept of connection, consider the following perspectives:

1) Core-distal awareness (connecting the core and the extremities)

In the beginning, we develop awareness and sensation of the body's surface. We tense or relax our muscles. We focus on the desired image of our body. We work on correcting its structure. We get a feel for the overall spacious distribution of the body-as-a-whole.

Initially, we know ourselves only in the most superficial ways – through our appearance and our basic sensory connections with the world around us. We define who we are by differentiating ourselves from everything else. This is a form of separation-consciousness that distinguishes 'me' from 'not me.' Body maps, forgotten parts, and the seeing alignment strategy prompt recognition of the distal aspect of this perspective.

As our 'core' or internal awareness awakens, we get a greater understanding for the details of the body's internal space. The center, the psoas, and the sensing alignment strategy help us make this connection. Hidden inside the body, we discover bones, internal organs, the respiratory process, circulation, and subtle energy channels. We begin to sense the inner workings of the body in relationship to the outer container or shell.

Each and every bodily system is a link in the continuum of physiological connections. This understanding yields a more accurate perception of the body and its parts. We begin to understand how the configuration of the parts determines the possibilities for the body-as-a-whole.

Remarkably, this internal awakening is reflected by a similar awakening in our emotional response. We will develop a greater capacity for tolerance, compassion, and honesty in all relationships, as well as a renewed interest in humanity. We will have a distinct sense of community and kinship. We might experience a connection to the animals and plants, and even to the galaxy. We will get a feel for how each of us, as a unique individual entity, fits into the bigger picture. As we come to know ourselves, we come to know others.

2) Inner-outer awareness (connecting the inner impulse and the outer expression)

The idea always comes first. The idea, or the inner form, refers to the psychological impulse. The inner form is expressed as an outer form, or a physical manifestation. This suggests that the impulse precedes the manifestation. Without an impulse, there would be no manifestation. The thought of movement precedes the movement. Intent precedes execution of intent. Outer expression is a result of the inner idea.

In yoga asana, we can visualize the pose as a preliminary mental event before we ever attempt the pose. The inner-outer perspective is the basic concept behind many forms of meditation. Another example of the inner-outer concept is the distinct feeling that we get from visiting different places. Each of us has personal preferences for certain cities, stores, restaurants, etc. We feel more comfortable in some places than we do in others. We subconsciously recognize the fact that our own impulses are in harmony or disharmony with the impulse that permeates that particular environment.

Any city or community represents a group of people that have come together with a shared impulse. That impulse is based on similar ideas regarding creation and intention. For example, the hustle and bustle of New York City produces a lively and provocative sensory experience that reflects the mindset of its inhabitants. Some visitors to the Big Apple will classify this lively nature as stimulating and energizing, while others will find it stressful and stifling. Their perception depends on how well the vibes of the city mesh with the internal rhythms of the individual.

In yoga, the inner-outer concept explains our preference for some poses or categories of poses over others. For the most part, we prefer the poses that are easy for us. We like poses that we can perform without struggle and without activation of the stress response. Subconsciously, we prefer these poses because we have confidence in our ability to perform this pose.

The presumption of certainty, based on an impulse of confidence, is expressed as ease or relative effortlessness in the body. But the inner-outer concept can also work against us. It can establish a self-defeating pattern based on the presumption of weakness or inaptitude. The presumption of uncertainty, based on an impulse of inferiority, is expressed as incapability or bodily distress.

3) Head-tail awareness (connecting the head and the spine/tail)

This concept involves keen awareness of the spinal column's position. Don't sell your spine short! This image should extend from the tip of the tailbone to seven inches above the crown of the head. The head-tail perspective activates a solid somatic awareness of the body's central channel. It affirms the spine's capacity for adaptation and repositioning. This is especially useful in asana, since the positioning for any posture revolves around the primary placement of the spine.

The head represents the thinking part of an organism. This is the part that makes decisions and partakes in contemplation. The spine and tail are the followers. These parts must work in conjunction with the head to – both literally and figuratively – provide support and expression.

Head-tapping and spinal rolling are two techniques that awaken head-tail awareness. To perform head-tapping, round the fingers and gently tap tap tap all over the surface of the head. This activity wakes up the scalp and skull. Spinal rolling is used to activate spinal energy. To perform spinal rolling, assume a tucked position and then rock and roll like a ball. This activity irons out kinks in the fascia, though at first the knots make the rolling awkward or uncomfortable.

Head-tapping   Spinal rolling

I always suggest that students perform spinal rolling with their eyes closed. This helps them get a feel for a changing gravitational situation without relying on the familiarity of a horizon-based orientation. Any pose that alters our traditional upright stance provides a valuable experience in head-tail awareness.

4) Stability-mobility (connecting the base of support and the action)

The entire entity, whether in motion or stillness, should always operate from a solid and steadfast base of support. The base of support grounds us. The base of support receives our weight and anchors us. Acknowledgement of the support structure and its relationship to gravity needs to be among our priorities.

Mobility represents the freedom of expansion and expression. Mobility is anchored in stability; therefore movement is anchored in a base of support. The moving or active body part (the part experiencing action or extension) is able to do so *because* of the 'roots' provided by the base of support.

5) Exertion-recuperation (connecting activity with relaxation)

How many times must we be reminded that we are not fighting a duel with the asana? Asana is not something that the body and mind must conquer or overcome. Yet the urge for competition and domination is deeply imbedded in our consciousness. Our achievement-oriented society teaches us that "If I try hard enough, I will win."

Balancing the tendency toward exertion with a fair share of recuperation provides a healthier perspective for both the psyche and the soma. The 'all work, no play' or 'hard work pays off' mentality is erroneous. Effort, willpower, and domination are not the path to perfection in a pose, and the need to rest is not a weakness. In asana, grace during perseverance is curtailed by the use of force. Paradoxically, excellence occurs when we surrender the ego's willfulness.

The natural cycles of exertion and recuperation help to maintain the integrity of the entity-as-a-whole. Periods of exertion must be balanced by periods of recuperation. The ability to alternate between the active and the passive is necessary to sustain health, energy, and continuous restoration. The exertion-recuperation perspective indicates the necessity for savasana – the corpse pose of complete rest and relaxation. This is why a moderate to extended period of rest during final relaxation is an integral part of any yoga class.

❖ Inquiry # 22: "Connected awareness"

Concept: In this inquiry, we examine the five perspectives of connected awareness – (1) core-distal, (2) inner-outer, (3) head-tail, (4) stability-mobility, and (5) exertion-recuperation in an integrated execution of the bow pose.

Bow pose

Inquiry # 22: "Connected awareness"

Directions: Perform the bow pose. Hold the pose for ten steady breaths or one minute. Notice the sensations in your body. Notice what made the pose seem hard. What body parts got tired? Which body parts were you most aware of, and which parts did you tend to ignore?

Discussion: In the bow pose, most people waste a lot of energy by putting forth an unnecessary amount of effort. They struggle and strain to lift the head, neck, shoulders, chest, feet, and legs up off the floor to create the backward arching position. This lifting-up approach quickly drains one's energy because it is a profound attempt to work against gravity.

Instead, we could approach the posture in a more moderate fashion by concentrating on a reduction of effort. To reduce both the amount and perception of effort, we must consciously release the body's weight downward into the navel center. In this way, the physical demands of lifting and arching the head, chest, legs, and feet is successfully counterbalanced by the mental focus on releasing the body's weight downward into the base of support. The navel center provides the core experience (all points connect downward to the navel), the inner awareness (the intent of groundedness), and serves as the midpoint for the connection between head and tail.

The navel center provides stability by acting as the body's base of support, and it balances the forces of exertion (lifting up) with recuperation (sinking down). When the active force of 'doing' is neutralized by the passive force of 'being,' we experience the somatic state of harmony. The balanced forces allow us to sustain the pose in an effortless manner.

Relationships are Connections

Now let's look at how relationships act as connections. The following principles of connection have to do with healing relationships through awareness and wholeness. The first principle involves relationship with the self, or knowing who you are. This precedes the second principle which pertains to relationship with others.

Connection Principle # 1

Inner connectivity (the self's experience of wholeness) is balanced by outer expressivity (personal expression or creativity). This means that the self's experience of wholeness is determined by its abilities for personal expression.

The inverse is also true – that the experience of the self is determined by your creative ability of self expression. In essence, *you are what you can express, and you can only express what you are.*

Connection Principle # 2

Outer connectivity (successful relationship) is balanced by inner expression (realization of self and understanding of universal truths). This means that successful relationship is determined by your degree of personal realization and understanding of universal truths.

It also means that your ability to reach out and make successful connections with others is determined by your personal relationship with the self. In essence, *your relationship with others is a reflection of your relationship with the self, and your relationship with the self is a reflection of your relationship with others.*

CHAPTER TWENTY

The Spirit of Yoga

There was one other extraordinary thing that happened during my early days as a young yoga student in California. I was healed by a pendulum. Unbelievable as it may sound, I am telling the truth. If it hadn't happened to me, I probably wouldn't have believed it!

I had suffered from stress-induced, chronic stomach aches since I was thirteen. After years of enduring painful symptoms, swallowing spoonfuls of antacids, and two trips to the emergency room, I was miraculously healed by this non-traditional method. In less than ten minutes, a small green pendulum that hung from a six inch string was all it took to find relief.

The abdominal sensation of screaming, stabbing pain was quickly reduced to no sensation at all. At first I was unsure of the stillness within my belly. Something I had grown accustomed to was surprisingly absent. Where was that familiar feeling of pain?

Absence of Sensation

We can clearly differentiate between the state of health, wholeness, and faith, and the state of sickness, fragmentation, and despair by exploring sensations that we feel in the soma. In sickness, we are excruciatingly aware of the body. It calls our attention to the negative symptoms associated with misery - aches, pains, congestion, and such. These sensations indicate that our bodily systems are out of balance. Symptoms are the mouthpiece of the somatic messenger. They loudly and relentlessly inform us that something is wrong. They are telling us that the body requires our attention.

All body systems are also active and functioning during the experience of health and happiness. But in the balanced state of wellness, the voice of the somatic messenger is surprisingly silent. During the harmonious experience of good health, mental energy need not be allocated toward pursuing a remedy for physical ailments. When we are in good health, we are free to immerse ourselves fully into our daily lives, relationships, and activities.

Surely all of us have noticed how the body responds to the receipt of joyous news. It reacts by embodying the state of happiness – by coming alive! Bountiful energy bubbles up - so much that it is often difficult to contain ourselves. Our bodies want and need to release this energy surge.

We want to explode into movement, to revel in some form of creative expression. We have to run, jump, dance, sing, or scream.

The energetic experience of a happy soma need not occur strictly as a reaction to outside influences. We can consciously cultivate this experience from within. An energetic yet blissful state of being reflects an absence of malice and a self that is not sorry.

The sensation of wholeness is an absence of sensation.

Absence of sensation is a scary feeling for many yoga students because it is unfamiliar and difficult to comprehend. Most of us are used to living with the day to day aggravations of little aches, pains, and minor illnesses such as the common cold. We function in spite of chronic fatigue from lack of adequate sleep.

Human bodies that operate at a suboptimal status are the norm. That is why even the momentary experience of a truly blissful state in which the body is balanced, united, whole, and healthy sometimes leaves us unsure – because we have no designated standard by which we can judge or rationalize this lack of sensational experience. This is also why a person that does attain the normal or natural level of health and happiness is considered to be exceptional.

Most of the sensations we feel during asana practice come from blockages and limitations. What we feel are the remaining points of resistance in the body. The somatic messenger is drawing our attention to the body part or parts that are out of sync. Like a trombone player who hits a sour note during a band performance, it is the sound or sensation of disharmony that gets our attention and prompts the question, "What was that? What's the problem?"

The lack of sensation that indicates the experience of wholeness is not an exclusively physical phenomenon. Neutrality of the mental state is an imperative aspect of the sensational void. The state of the breath will also function in its most natural rhythm. A calm mind, a relaxed body, and a steady breath are the components of neutrality.

Given these circumstances, the soma will register a unified, natural state of being. This healthy blend is both pleasing and comfortable. Absence of sensation indicates a healthy organism that bears no unnecessary tension and harbors no regrets.

Let's look at another example of how the psycho-somatic connection affects our perception of sensation. Suppose you have a slight but chronic pain in your left hip. This hip hurts whenever you take a step forward with your left foot. It hurts no matter what position you sit in. It even hurts when you are sleeping. Though you are not really aware of it, much of your physical and psychological energy is spent protecting the left hip from further pain. Your subconscious mind must remain vigilant. Over time, living in this guarded state is both mentally and physically exhausting.

Then one glorious morning you wake up and your hip doesn't hurt. But you don't even notice or acknowledge the absence of the pain. You just get out of bed and go about your business *without even realizing that you are pain-free*! Your mind is completely captivated by the activities of the day, and you are fully engrossed in whatever you are doing. You might notice that you feel unnaturally productive and happy. You might even say to yourself, "I'm having a really good day!" Much later you finally acknowledge that you are feeling good because your body is pain-free. The absence of that nagging negative sensation liberated a lot of physical and mental energy that is now available for constructive use.

When we are healthy and happy, we are more or less unaware of our bodies because they function with ease and absence of sensation. A healthy body is a comfortable body that has no need to send somatic messages of tightness, limitations, obstructions, discomfort, fatigue, and pain. It does not need to remind us to be careful, guarded, and protective. It doesn't trap us in denial or fear. A healthy body indicates a healthy mental attitude, both of which are advantageous for the process of personal transformation.

Self-discovery through Asana

Asana training supports the process of self-discovery by improving our sensory awareness. It helps us to be aware of important information that we have previously overlooked. Enhanced sensory awareness improves the accuracy of our impressions so that we can make reasonable deductions. We remain balanced and whole, no matter what changes take place in our internal or external environment.

Asana can even lead us to different experiences of consciousness. The three statements listed below suggest three possible experiences of consciousness during contemplation in the pose. Each represents a different way of being. One is not necessarily better than another. They are just different perspectives of the meditative experience. Each perspective progresses toward the specialized experience of self as soma.

1. I am my body in the pose, with these thoughts, near these people, in this room.

2. I am my body in the pose.

3. I am my body. (I am the soma.)

Statement # 1 is the most rudimentary perspective of the meditative experience. It indicates separation of the Participant and the Observer. This experience is based on the body's placement in a certain location, a certain position, and at a certain time. The student's meditative experience consists of observing himself in relationship to his external environment. "I am here. She is there. The table is over there." The first meditative experience indicates awareness of the self based on its relationship with others.

The difference between Statement # 1 and the other two statements is the extinguishment of time and place. As the Participant and the Observer begin to merge, the student's experience becomes progressively freed of distractions (Statement # 2). Finally, the perspective becomes more sharply aligned to a singular focus (Statement # 3). In the third perspective, the student has successfully merged the Participant and the Observer.

The specific difference between Statements # 2 and # 3 is the nullification of gravity. In Statement # 2 the student perceives his body in relationship to gravity. He can tell if he is positioned vertically, horizontally, flexed at the waist, etc. He feels his body's reaction to the force of gravity.

In Statement # 3, the student transcends the gravitational force. In this case, up and down no longer matter. He perceives the position of his body, but the body could be floating or sinking. There is no longer a sensation of lying on the right side or left side, facing down or up, being inverted or being upright. This experience is based solely on inner sensation and the wisdom of the body. Relativity is no longer acknowledged. To reach this meditative experience, the yoga student has come a long way.

But there is a further state of mastery that lies beyond the identification of self as soma. In this experience, the student transcends the limitations of the physical and the mental. The boundaries of his own body dissolve. There is no longer a recollection of the packaging that binds him to this dimension and this existence. He experiences a formless state of consciousness that states simply "I am." There is no longer any sensation at all. There is only consciousness.

At some point, all individuals will realize that asana is not a performance art and it is not image-oriented. They will realize that we don't practice yoga asana just to perfect the pose. On the contrary, we practice yoga asana because it has a direct effect on our lives. Asana provides a practical, somatic path toward contacting the body's consciousness and generating self-transformation. By listening to the wisdom of the body, we have the opportunity to enhance the quality of our lives.

Our goals need not be lofty. In fact, the best goals are prudent, modest, and non-specific. They might include simple, basic, or generic ideals such as to remain relatively peaceful, to have a good day, and to be a positive influence on others. The most productive goals in asana are also generic, such as to practice safely, consciously, and regularly. These deliberately vague goals indicate our faith that the universe will provide for us in the way that is best for us. By making no specific demands or desires, we give the universe a lot of leeway toward satisfying our request.

I have learned to appreciate the truth of a statement that I first encountered many, many years ago. "The way you practice asana is the way you live your life."

In regard to your life and to your asana practice, consider the following questions. Do you 'join in the dance' everyday, or do you partake only when the spirit moves you? Does it excite you or do you consider it an unwanted chore? Do you try to exert your will, or are you willing to cooperate? Do you meet the moment without expectations? Do you do it happily and joyously, or are you often frustrated, confused, or bored? Are your intentions pure-hearted, or are you pursuing an agenda? Are you relaxed or are you tense? Are you a pacifist, or do you have a need to conquer and control? Are both your body and mind in attendance? Are you committed to making it meaningful?

Symbolically, what we consider to be most important in asana is what we consider to be most important in our lives. This means that what we seek to master in asana is the same thing that we (probably unconsciously) seek to master in our lives. Whether that lesson is flexibility, strength, balance, stability, perseverance, connection, wholeness, relationships, faith, freedom, self-acceptance, self-reliance, or personal responsibility, how we practice asana directly reflects our current state of being. On the flipside, the part of asana that we most dislike, that we'd rather avoid, and in which we lack competency reflects our inappropriate or immature tendencies.

I have studied somatic concepts related to yoga asana and I have spent years working through the healing process of self-discovery within my own body. Through my experiential research, I have come to the conclusion that we are able to learn our lessons in somatic re-education very, very well. Somatic learning is much more than temporary, transient, or provisional. Yet it would be premature to state that these changes are always permanent and absolute.

During rare moments of emergency, those hard-wired, genetically-inspired, reflexive responses occasionally manage to resurface. Perhaps at a very deep level of consciousness, the seed of the original habit still exists. In an embodied situation, some somatic tendencies might be deeper and older than the hour of birth itself.

We began our life's journey with certain genetic predispositions. These predispositions are a part of who we were born to be. This is the gift of our genetic heritage. The fact that consciously acquired transformation doesn't necessarily produce genetic alterations should in no way imply failure. Nor should it diminish the individual's dedication toward the path of personal evolution.

Much of the significance regarding conscious somatic re-education is *how it impacts the next generation.* The children of the next generation observe, listen, and learn from our behaviors and dialogues. If we cultivate, nurture, and display our new and improved selves, we become meritorious role models. We become people of excellence and value. By seeking transformation of the self, we make a significant contribution to the evolution of the species.

Though the sum of human consciousness is composed of approximately 6.4 billion separate embodiments, the nature of humanity is built on their connection and community. Each of us is a powerful and potent part of the continuum that is permeated by the supreme life force. As we journey into self-discovery, we have the opportunity to change and improve. We can determine who and what we are through conscious observation and active participation.

This continual process of 'insights put into action' results in self-sufficiency and intrinsic satisfaction. We relearn our natural ability to interact with our internal and external environments in a responsible and meaningful manner. By appreciating the value of different perspectives and continual change, we grow and evolve. A change in the individual is the way to start changing the whole world, for the whole world is affected by the evolution of each of its individual parts.

Welcome Memories

No matter which path my yoga students chose, I hope that they will think back on our days spent together and smile. I know that I will be forever thankful to my first yoga teacher for introducing me to yoga asana. Back at that scientific yoga studio in southern California, back when I was 22-and-a-half years old, this little Columbian man's presence was an important part of my life. He had a pure heart and a positive attitude. He demonstrated qualities that I wanted to acquire. He embodied the spirit of yoga. We, the students, adored him. In his classes, we were loved and accepted unconditionally. I was lucky to have found him.

"We shall not cease from exploration, and at the end of all our exploring
we will arrive where we started and know the place
for the very first time."
~T.S. Eliot

Enlighten Your Body

Bibliography

Alexander, G. 1985. *Eutony.* Great Neck, NY: Felix Morrow.

Baier, K. Iyengar and the Yoga Tradition. [article on-line] http://www.iyengar-yoga.com; Internet; accessed 7 May 2003. Original article in *BKS Iyengar Yoga Teachers' Association News Magazine,* Winter 1995.

Brooks, C. 1986. *Sensory Awareness: The Redefining of Experiencing.* Great Neck, NY: Felix Morrow. Original edition, New York, NY: Viking, 1974.

Calais-Germain, B. 1993. *Anatomy of Movement.* Engl ed., Seattle, WA: Eastland Press.

Dart, R. 1996. *Skill and Poise.* London: STAT Books.

Feldenkrais, M. 1990. *Awareness through Movement.* New York, NY: HarperCollins. Original edition, New York, NY: HarperCollins, 1972.

Hanna, T. Clinical Somatic Education: A New Discipline in the Field of Health Care. [article on-line] http://www.somaticscenter.com/library/htl-cse.html; Internet; accessed 8 May 2003.Original article in *SOMATICS,* Volume VIII, Autumn/Winter 1990-91.

_____ 1988. *Somatics: Reawakening the Mind's Control of Movement, Flexibility, and Health.* Reading, MA: Perseus Books.

Heller, J., and W. Henkin. 1991. *Bodywise.* Oakland, CA: Wingbow Press. Original edition, New York: Jeremy Tarcher, 1986.

Johnson, D. H., ed. 1995. *Bone, Breath, & Gesture: Practices of Embodiment.* Berkeley, CA: North Atlantic Books.

Jones, F. P. 1997. *Freedom to Change.* 3d ed., London: Mouritz.

Koch, L. 1997. *The Psoas Book.* 2d ed., Felton, CA: Guinea Pig Publications.

Kramer, J. Yoga as Self-Transformation. [article on-line] http://www.whitelotus.org/kramer4.html; Internet; accessed 2 July 2000. Original article in *Yoga Journal,* May/June, 1980.

Leri, D. Learning How to Learn. [article on-line] http://www.semiophysics.com/learning.htm; Internet; accessed 26 May 2003. Original article in *Gnosis*, Fall 1993.

Maisel, E. 1969. *The Resurrection of the Body: The Writings of F. Matthias Alexander.* New York, NY: Dell Publishing.

Middendorf, I. 1990. *The Perceptible Breath: A Breathing Science.* Paderborn, Germany: Junfermann-Verlag.

Paton, D. Dance and the 4 Stages of Mastery. [article on-line] http://www.ltdance.com/4_stages.html; Internet; accessed 7 May 2003.

Varughese, Suma. Body and Beyond. *Life Positive.* March 2003, 50-62.

Yuasa, Y. 1987. *The Body: Toward an Eastern Mind-Body Theory.* Albany, NY: State University of New York Press.

References

Part One

Yuasa, Y. 1987. *The Body: Toward an Eastern Mind-Body Theory.* Albany, NY: State University of New York Press, 10.

Ibid., 85.

Enlighten Your Body